MW00614983

U.S. PUBLIC HEALTH SERVICE OFFICER'S GUIDE

Leadership, Protocol, & Service Standards

The U.S. Public Health Service Mission

Protecting, promoting, and advancing the health and safety of the Nation

PHS OFFICER'S GUIDE

□□□□□

Leadership, Protocol, & Service Standards

SECOND EDITION

CAPT James E. Knoben (Ret.)

CAPT Alice D. Knoben

U.S. PUBLIC HEALTH SERVICE

Copyright © 2014 by the

PHS Commissioned Officers Foundation
for the Advancement of Public Health

The authors have written this book in their private capacity. The views
expressed are those of the authors and do not necessarily represent official
positions of the Office of the Surgeon General, U.S. Public Health Service,
and/or the Department of Health and Human Services.

SECOND EDITION

ISBN 978-0-9773149-3-5

Distribution by the

Commissioned Officers Association of the U.S. Public Health Service
8201 Corporate Drive, Suite 200
Landover, Maryland 20797

Printed in the United States of America

CONTENTS

Foreword		*ix*
Preface		*xi*
Acknowledgments		*xiii*

CHAPTER ONE   Uniformed Service Essentials 1

The US Public Health Service	*1*
Culture, Tradition, and Protocol	*3*
Personnel, Ranks and Insignia	*5*
Appearance, Uniform, Award Standards	*13*

CHAPTER TWO   Leadership Principles 25

USPHS Core Values	*25*
Officership	*26*
Leadership Theory	*28*
Leadership Competencies	*34*
Leadership Principles	*36*
PHS Leadership Competency Model	*40*

CHAPTER THREE   Courtesy & Protocol 41

Address & Greeting	*41*
Coming to Attention	*44*
Flag Etiquette	*45*
Headgear	*48*
Position of Honor	*49*
Precedence of Military Services	*49*
Rendering Honors	*50*
Saluting	*50*

CHAPTER FOUR   Official Ceremony Protocol 54

Awards Ceremony	*54*
Change of Command Ceremony	*57*
Promotion Ceremony	*60*
Retirement Ceremony	*63*
Military Funeral Honors	*70*

CHAPTER FIVE Social Ceremony Protocol 73

Dining-In & Dining-Out	73
Official Dinners and Receptions	80
Military Wedding Ceremony	87

CHAPTER SIX Special Duty Positions 89

Aide-de-Camp & Escort Officer	89
Service Boards	97
Chief Professional Officer	98
Honor Cadre	100
Junior Officer Advisory Group	103
Liaison, Commissioned Corps	104
Minority Officers Liaison Council	105
Music Ensemble	106
Professional Advisory Committee	108
Protocol Officer	110
Readiness Force	112
Surgeon General's Policy Advisory Council	116

CHAPTER SEVEN Communications 117

Business Cards	117
Calls & Cards	120
Conversation	121
Correspondence	123
Greetings & Introductions	127
Presentations & Speaking	130
Telecommunications	132

CHAPTER EIGHT Meetings 134

The Chairperson	135
The Participants	136
Office Appointments	137
Conventions	138
Parliamentary Procedure	138

CHAPTER NINE Table Protocol 141

Table Settings	141
Table Manners	146
Restaurant Dining	149

CHAPTER TEN U.S. Public Health Service 129

Mission	152
Organization	153
Office of the Surgeon General	154
Agency Assignments	158
Regular and Ready Reserve Corps	162
USPHS History	163
PHS Flag	166
PHS Seal	166
PHS CC Seal	166
PHS March	167
PHS Coin	167

CHAPTER ELEVEN Uniformed Service Organizations 143

Department of Defense	168
U.S. Air Force	170
U.S. Army	172
U.S. Coast Guard	173
U.S. Marine Corps	175
U.S. Navy	176
National Oceanic and Atmospheric Administration Corps	177

Abbreviations, Acronyms, & Glossary 179

Selected References 183

Appendices 185

A.	Planning for Awards, Change of Command, Promotion, Retirement Ceremony	186
B.	Planning a Dining-Out	189
C.	Planning a Formal Reception	191
D.	Planning for a Distinguished Visitor	193

Index 195

FOREWORD

In 2014, the U.S. PUBLIC HEALTH SERVICE COMMISSIONED CORPS celebrated its quasquicentennial anniversary, commemorated historical achievements such as the 50th Anniversary of the first Surgeon General's Report on Smoking and Health, and continued to lead by example by becoming the first uniformed service to go tobacco free while in uniform. The Commissioned Corps is mighty small, but we do it all! We are the only uniformed service in the world comprised of a health-related professional cadre dedicated to public health. Our Commissioned Corps has met and continues to overcome challenges with skill, professionalism and optimism. Our mission has never been more compelling and our value to the Nation never more evident. Throughout our long and proud history, the public health achievements to which we have so greatly contributed have prevented disease and improved the health and safety of our nation.

As Commissioned Corps Officers we should always remember our founders, those defining moments of our history, and the bold leaders that have come before us and those that lead our Corps today. Having a historical perspective on our service allows us to understand both our foundation and our evolution over time. Eric Shinseki, 7th U.S. Secretary of Veterans Affairs, once said, "If you dislike change, you're going to dislike irrelevance even more." We have proven to our nation, agencies, and sister services that we are a relevant uniformed service by working side by side on the important mission to protect, promote, and advance the health and safety of our nation. As good officers, we embrace change and we remain good stewards of our Commissioned Corps.

The U.S. Public Health Service Commissioned Corps currently has a Commissioned Corps Issuance System, but does not have a Commissioned Corps specific Protocol Policy. However, the *Public Health Service Officer's Guide* is an excellent reference in this area and provides an opportunity for officers to enhance their knowledge base regardless of rank and years of service. The *Guide* is an amalgamation of protocol policy from all uniformed services representative of a comprehensive and organized review of courtesies, customs, protocols, standards, and other pertinent information of benefit to all Commissioned Officers. We all should use this guide, with other resources available to us, and continue to represent our service with pride and hold true to our traditions, customs, protocols, and the social etiquette that binds us to our sister services and significantly impacts our esprit de corps.

Boris D. Lushniak, MD, MPH
RADM, USPHS
Acting Surgeon General

My heartfelt gratitude to CAPT (ret.) James E. Knoben and CAPT Alice Knoben – you are both the epitome of officership. Thank you for the dedication, commitment and devotion to the U.S. Public Health Service Commissioned Corps and the release of the 2nd edition of the Public Health Service Officer's Guide.

PREFACE

One thing I know: the only ones among you who will be really happy are those who will have sought and found how to serve.

Albert Schweitzer

U.S. Public Health Service commissioned officers have a unique opportunity to serve their fellow Americans and people throughout the world. Since its inception, PHS officers have provided healthcare services and confronted public health issues with compassion, resolve and vision. Today, the Commissioned Corps has the breadth of expertise that places it in a leadership position to protect, promote and advance public health.

The increasing threat of natural and manmade disasters compels the Commissioned Corps to more effectively address public health challenges on both a national and global scale. These responsibilities involve a greater level of preparedness, knowledge about providing health-related care in differing circumstances and diverse cultures, and interoperability with other uniformed and civilian personnel. Such cooperative effort requires that PHS officers be knowledgeable about uniformed service customs and protocols. All uniformed services provide officers with knowledge of protocol and service tradition to enhance their officers' effectiveness, promote esprit de corps, and effect a favorable working environment that impacts positively on overall productivity and corporate image.

PHS officers must also have the requisite leadership capabilities to effectively perform their duties. This new edition of the *Public Health Service Officer's Guide* has been thoroughly updated and, significantly, provides PHS officers with a new chapter on Leadership theory, competencies and principles. This reflects the importance which the USPHS Commissioned Corps has placed on ensuring that its officers are knowledgeable about leadership principles and are able to meet the public health challenges of an increasingly complex and interdependent world.

The integration of uniformed service protocol with social consciousness is reflected by the adage *"an officer and a gentleman (-woman)."* Uniformed service officers are judged by how they conduct themselves and relate to

xi

others, as well as their professional competence. The world is connected like never before and, for PHS officers, cultural awareness and understanding of social protocol may be essential in realizing successful health diplomacy.

The *Public Health Service Officer's Guide*, 2nd edition, provides officers with a comprehensive, yet concise information resource on uniformed service and PHS leadership, protocol, traditions, service standards and etiquette that will complement their heritage. Heritage of the Public Health Service – its history, customs and traditions – is a foundation upon which its officers continue the legacy of unparalleled accomplishment. It is hoped that by using this book, PHS officers will achieve a more rewarding professional life which will, in turn, serve to strengthen the Public Health Service Commissioned Corps as it advances in this new millennium.

ACKNOWLEDGMENTS

The preparation of this new edition of the *PHS Officer's Guide* was a challenging, yet very worthwhile endeavor. The support of the Office of the Surgeon General in responding to periodic requests for information has been important to the book's completion. We want to recognize Rear Admiral Boris Lushniak, who wrote the Foreword, for his exemplary leadership as Acting Surgeon General, and former Surgeon General Richard Carmona, who wrote the first edition Foreword, for his steadfast support of the Commissioned Corps. Our sincere thanks to PHS officers who reviewed areas of the book in which they have particular expertise, including Rear Admiral (ret.) Jerry Michael, Rear Admiral (ret.) Bob Williams, Rear Admiral Scott Giberson, Captain Bruce Tierney, and CDR Rhondalyn Cox. All reviewers' comments were of immense value in ensuring the accuracy and readability of the book.

Captain (ret.) Gene Migliaccio, President of the PHS Commissioned Officers Foundation for the Advancement of Public Health, and Trustees of the Foundation deserve special appreciation for providing support to produce the book for PHS officers. And, our thanks to RADM (ret.) Mike Milner and the COF Executive Staff who were instrumental in getting the new edition published, including John McElligott, Captain (ret.) Jerry Farrell, USN, and COL (ret.) Jim Currie, USA.

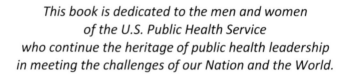

This book is dedicated to the men and women
of the U.S. Public Health Service
who continue the heritage of public health leadership
in meeting the challenges of our Nation and the World.

CHAPTER ONE

UNIFORMED SERVICE ESSENTIALS

The commitment to a uniformed service involves a professional and service life that is distinctly different from civilian professions. This chapter provides an overview of the U.S. Public Health Service, its formation and mission; the importance of tradition and protocol in the uniformed services; uniformed service personnel, ranks and insignia; and, uniform standards.

THE U.S. PUBLIC HEALTH SERVICE
CULTURAL COMPETENCE, TRADITIONS, PROTOCOL
PERSONNEL, RANKS, INSIGNIA
APPEARANCE, UNIFORM, AWARD STANDARDS

The U.S. Public Health Service

The U.S. Public Health Service Commissioned Corps (USPHS) is one of seven uniformed services of the United States of America that protect the welfare of our Nation. Each of the uniformed services contributes in its own unique way to realize that overarching mission. The USPHS is distinct, due to its composition of an all-officer Corps and comprehensive public health mission, which is a vital component of national security and international in scope.

The USPHS is led by the U.S. Surgeon General, with administrative and policy oversight by the Assistant Secretary for Health in the Department of Health and Human Services (HHS). The Surgeon General, who is considered the chief health educator for the Nation, provides leadership and operational command of the Corps. The USPHS is a multidisciplinary force comprised primarily of health care and related professionals within eleven professional categories. They work in clinical service and public health leadership roles in an array of federal government agencies. Responsibilities include health care delivery; disease control and prevention; biomedical research; and regulation of food, drugs, and medical devices. Known as "America's Health Responders," USPHS personnel also serve on emergency preparedness and response teams that deploy to public health crises and national emergencies.

HHS administers the major health program of the federal government, known as the Public Health Service, of which the USPHS Commissioned Corps is an essential component. The Public Health Service is comprised of eight major agencies with over 300 programs, covering a wide range of critically important activities. The broad mission of HHS and the Public Health Service is to provide essential health services and protect the health of the Nation. HHS currently employs about 70,000 Civil Service and 6,800 commissioned officers to accomplish that mission. Two thousand of those officers serve outside of HHS in eight other U.S. Departments and in 800 locations worldwide.

Professional Officer
The decision to accept a commission in the USPHS Commissioned Corps is of considerable importance, due to the fact that it is usually a life-long career choice. USPHS officers enter the service with similar constraints, obligations, performance expectations, rights and privileges of officers in other uniformed services. As a commissioned officer with essential public health responsibilities, the USPHS is an organization that is professional and collegial, and at the same time supportive of an Officer Corps.

Commissioned officers serve in two supporting, yet integrated roles – one, as an expert in their chosen professional field, and the other as a uniformed service professional. The concept of the professional officer reflects the distinction of receiving a presidential commission to serve the Nation; a commitment to "service before self"; the acceptance of high ethical standards, personal responsibility and accountability for your actions; and, the expectation that all officers show leadership and dedication in the performance of their duties. Taken together, these are profound obligations that constitute the essence of being an officer, or *officership*. PHS officers must always be competent practitioners of their specialized knowledge and skills and, at the same time, be well trained and capable of serving as a public health leader and accomplishing the organization's overarching public health mission.

PHS/USPHS FORMATION & MISSION
The HHS Public Health Service was effectively established in 1798, with passage of the *Act for the Relief of Sick and Disabled Seamen*. The *Act* led to construction of a network of maritime hospitals that were administratively centralized in 1870 with creation of the Marine Hospital Service (MHS). In 1871, the position of Supervising Surgeon (later Surgeon General) was created to administer the Service. MHS activities greatly expanded over subsequent years until, in 1912, its name was changed to the Public Health Service.

The Commissioned Corps was formalized in 1889 with passage of *An Act to Regulate Appointments in the Marine Hospital Service of the United States*, which set appointment standards and established the Corps along military lines, including officer reassignment to meet the needs of the MHS. Over the intervening years, the Public Health Service and the USPHS Commissioned

Corps have built a record of biomedical and public health achievement that is unequalled throughout the world. PHS officers receive this heritage upon being commissioned, and it serves as both a mark of distinction and an inspiration for new generations of officers to carry on the tradition of extraordinary accomplishment in enhancing public health for all Americans and for the betterment of humankind. In keeping with that tradition, the MISSION of the U.S. Public Health Service Commissioned Corps is to

protect, promote, and advance the health and safety of our Nation.

The Commissioned Corps achieves its mission through:

- rapid and effective response to public health needs,
- leadership and excellence in public health practices, and
- the advancement of public health science.

Culture, Traditions, and Protocol

CULTURAL COMPETENCE

In most all societies and major institutions, there are prescribed behavioral norms, practices, and ceremonies to mark life events. These observances or traditions derive from beliefs, customs and ideas that may have evolved over hundreds of years. Their importance transcends the mere collective practice of a form of conduct or activity. Rather, when morally-based, such practice weaves a social fabric throughout the society that joins people together in greater harmony, promotes the general welfare, and provides a bond with past and future generations. These shared behavioral values, along with a myriad of other elements that a group may adopt (e.g., language, architecture, cuisine), constitute the *culture* of the group or society.

In today's global community, socio-cultural understanding is increasingly a prerequisite in order for institutions and individuals to operate most effectively. Uniformed services, in particular, recognize the importance of such competencies with respect to mission accomplishment. Indeed, uniformed services, themselves, represent a unique culture, and such understanding is essential to operational success both within and outside these organizations.

Cultural competency is a developmental process that involves learning about one's own cultural values and biases, as well as the culture of others. Individuals and organizations attain proficiency in applying such understanding in order to effectively interact with persons from different cultural/ethnic backgrounds and in multicultural settings. The integration of uniformed service personnel, including PHS officers in clinical roles, with patients and collaborative partners on a local, regional, national and global scale requires that its members develop a solid grounding in cross-cultural competence.

SERVICE TRADITIONS

The word *tradition* derives from the Latin *tradere*, or "handing down/over"; thus, traditions are passed from one generation to the next. Traditions generally evolve slowly, and may be altered in the context of adapting to the changing needs and/or views of a group or society. Uniformed services are national institutions that place great emphasis on the observance of tradition, including customs and protocol. Traditions and heritage represent those experiences of the uniformed services and its members that are most valued, stand the test of time and are passed forward. Protocol includes the military courtesies and customs that show respect for others and foster good human relationships.

Heritage

The heritage of each uniformed service reflects profoundly on their corporate identities. Service heritage has many facets, among which are experiences relating to the institution itself, the environment in which it operates (e.g., nautical customs of the U.S. Navy), the historical record of the institution in carrying out its mission, and individual or group feats of noteworthy accomplishment or heroism. Such heritage includes the traditions and customs that impart esprit de corps and individual pride in being a member of a particular uniformed service. This heritage is at once a foundation and an inspiration for present-day uniformed service members to meet challenges with the courage and resolve shown by their forebears.

As with other uniformed services, the heritage of the U.S. Public Health Service Commissioned Corps is far reaching and significant in terms of its impact on the well-being of its citizens and people around the world. The history of both the Public Health Service organization and the USPHS Commissioned Corps is exceptional, and officers are the beneficiaries of that record of public health leadership and continue in that tradition today.

CUSTOMS AND PROTOCOL

There are customs and traditions shared by all uniformed services. These relate to the protocol, ceremonies, social and service standards that personnel learn upon joining a uniformed service. Such customs and protocol foster and strengthen interactions among service members. They may be modified to reflect the distinctive characteristics of each service and changed periodically in response to new trends, yet all are meant to facilitate and enrich a person's professional career and social interactions within and outside the uniformed service.

Military/uniformed service courtesy, such as the proper forms of address ("Sir", "Ma'am", "Captain"), rendering a salute, coming to attention, is an integral part of all uniformed services, and observance is required of all service personnel. The importance of these protocols also relates to uniformed service interoperability, whereby members of different services are able to work effectively together. Interoperability at the operational and tactical levels is essential, often requiring specialized joint operations training.

The value of embracing custom and tradition in uniformed service life has been reaffirmed throughout history. PHS commissioned officers who understand the significance of doing so will benefit greatly.

Personnel, Ranks and Insignia

There are seven uniformed services of the United States: the Air Force, Army, Coast Guard, Marine Corps, and Navy, which constitute the Armed Forces; and, the National Oceanic and Atmospheric Administration Commissioned Corps and Public Health Service Commissioned Corps. Within the seven services are specific categories of personnel: commissioned officers, warrant officers, noncommissioned officers and enlisted personnel.

Commissioned Officers

Commissioned officers represent the management and leadership within each uniformed service. Officers must have a bachelor's degree prior to commissioning, and may need a master's degree to be promoted. Most officers are commissioned through programs such as the military service academies (Air Force Academy at Colorado Springs, U.S. Military Academy at West Point, Coast Guard Academy at New London, Naval Academy at Annapolis), Reserve Officer Training Corps, Officer Candidate School, or Officer Training School (Air Force). There are ten commissioned officer grades:

Army, Marine Corps, Air Force
> Pay Grades 0-1 to 0-3: *Company grade officers*
> Pay Grades 0-4 to 0-6: *Field grade officers*
> Pay Grades 0-7 to 0-10: *General officers*

Navy, Coast Guard, PHS, NOAA
> Pay Grades 0-1 to 0-4: *Junior officers*
> Pay Grades 0-5 to 0-6: *Senior officers*
> Pay Grades 0-7 to 0-10: *Flag officers*

Military officers may be generally classified as line and non-line officers. Unrestricted line officers are trained combat specialists, whereas non-line officers are staff officers with specialty training (e.g., Supply Corps).

Warrant Officers

Warrant officers may receive direct warrant commissions or be advanced from the enlisted ranks based on training and experience. Although not required, many warrant officers have college degrees. There are five warrant officer grades. These officers hold warrants and are technical experts and specialists in certain capabilities or technologies, and serve as "middle managers" within the military structure. Upon promotion to Chief Warrant Officer (W-2 to W-5), they become commissioned warrant officers. There are no warrant officers in the Air Force.

Noncommissioned Officers

Noncommissioned officers serve as supervisors within a specialty, and as trainers and leaders. Upon reaching the E-4/E-5 through E-9 grades, enlisted personnel may achieve a status known as the *noncommissioned officer* (NCO). NCO eligibility begins at the grade E-4/5 in the Army (corporal/sergeant), E-5 in the Air Force (staff sergeant), and E-4 in the Marine Corps (corporal). The equivalent to NCO in the Navy and Coast Guard is the petty officer, which begins at the grade E-4 (petty officer third class). Through a competitive process, NCOs in the top three grades, E-7, E-8, and E-9, are deemed to be senior NCOs, or chief petty officers in the Navy and Coast Guard, who hold leadership roles. The top E-9 levels are reserved for the senior enlisted person of each uniformed service, who serves as the spokesperson and chief advisor to the Secretary for their respective enlisted force.

Enlisted Personnel

Enlisted personnel are required to have a high school diploma to join the military services. Following basic training, enlisted personnel are provided specialized training to perform the front-line jobs. There are nine enlisted pay grades, E-1 through E-9. Those in pay grades E-1 through E-3 are usually in training status (basic, specialized, advanced) or on their first assignment. The term used to identify a military person's specialty is *Air Force specialty* (Air Force), *military occupational specialty* (Army and Marine Corps), or *rating* (Navy). In the Navy, a rating badge on the uniform combines a unique rating insignia with the pay grade insignia (symbol above the stripes/chevrons).

RANKS AND INSIGNIA

The badges of rank have evolved over thousands of years of military history. Beginning with the Revolutionary War, American ranks and insignia were designed as adaptations of the British tradition. The specific ranks and insignia used among the uniformed services vary. Generally, the U.S. Coast Guard, Navy, NOAA, and Public Health Service have the same ranks and insignia for commissioned personnel and the enlisted (Coast Guard and Navy) personnel. Among the U.S. Air Force, Army, and Marine Corps, ranks and insignia are the same for commissioned personnel, but differ for the enlisted personnel. Each service has a unique service crest. (See the Charts, *Rank Insignia,* pages 7-12.)

ENLISTED RANK INSIGNIA

	ARMY	NAVY, COAST GRD	MARINE CORPS	AIR FORCE
E1	Private	Seaman Recruit (SR)	Private	Airman Basic
E2	Private E-2 (PV2)	Seaman Apprentice (SA)	Private First Class (PFC)	Airman (Amn)
E3	Private First Class (PFC)	Seaman (SN)	Lance Corporal (LCpl)	Airman First Class (A1C)
E4	Corporal (CPL) · Specialist (SPC)	Petty Officer Third Class(PO3)	Corporal (Cpl)	Senior Airman (SrA)
E5	Sergeant (SGT)	Petty Officer Second Class (PO2)	Sergeant (Sgt)	Staff Sergeant (SSgt)
E6	Staff Sergeant (SSG)	Petty Officer First Class (PO1)	Staff Sergeant (SSgt)	Technical Sergeant (TSgt)

ENLISTED RANK INSIGNIA *(Continued)*

	ARMY	NAVY, COAST GRD	MARINE CORPS	AIR FORCE

	ARMY		NAVY, COAST GRD		MARINE CORPS		AIR FORCE	
E7	Sergeant First Class (SFC)		Chief Petty Officer (CPO)		Gunnery Sergeant (GySgt)		Master Sergeant (MSgt)	First Sergeant
E8	Master Sergeant (MSG)	First Sergeant (1SG)	Senior Chief Petty Officer (SCPO)		Master Sergeant (MSgt)	First Sergeant	Senior Master Sergeant (SMSgt)	First Sergeant
E9	Sergeant Major (SGM)	Command Sergeant Major (CSM)	Master Chief Petty Officer (MCPO)	Fleet/Command Master Chief Petty Officer	Sergeant Major (SgtMaj)	Master Gunnery Sergeant (MGySgt)	Chief Master Sergeant (CMSgt)	First Sergeant	Command Chief Master Sergeant (CCM)
E9	Sergeant Major of the Army (SMA)		Master Chief Petty Officer of the Navy (MCPON) and Coast Guard (MCPOCG)		Sergeant Major of the Marine Corps (SgtMajMC)		Chief Master Sergeant of the Air Force (CMSAF)	

WARRANT OFFICER RANK INSIGNIA

	ARMY	NAVY, CG	MARINE CORPS	AIR FORCE
W1	Warrant Officer 1 WO1	USN Warrant Officer 1 — WO1	Warrant Officer 1 WO	NO WARRANT
W2	Chief Warrant Officer 2 CW2	USN Chief Warrant Officer 2 — CWO2 / USCG	Chief Warrant Officer 2 CWO2	NO WARRANT
W3	Chief Warrant Officer 3 CW3	USN Chief Warrant Officer 3 — CWO3 / USCG	Chief Warrant Officer 3 CWO3	NO WARRANT
W4	Chief Warrant Officer 4 CW4	USN Chief Warrant Officer 4 — CWO4 / USCG	Chief Warrant Officer 4 CWO4	NO WARRANT
W5	Chief Warrant Officer CW5	USN Chief Warrant Officer CWO5	Chief Warrant Officer 5 CWO5	NO WARRANT

COMMISSIONED OFFICER RANK INSIGNIA

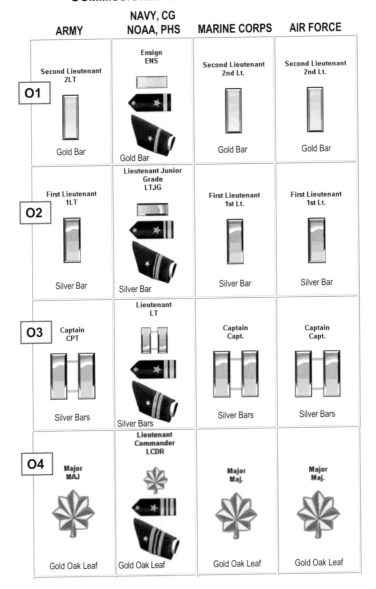

ARMY	NAVY, CG NOAA, PHS	MARINE CORPS	AIR FORCE
O1 Second Lieutenant 2LT — Gold Bar	Ensign ENS — Gold Bar	Second Lieutenant 2nd Lt. — Gold Bar	Second Lieutenant 2nd Lt. — Gold Bar
O2 First Lieutenant 1LT — Silver Bar	Lieutenant Junior Grade LTJG — Silver Bar	First Lieutenant 1st Lt. — Silver Bar	First Lieutenant 1st Lt. — Silver Bar
O3 Captain CPT — Silver Bars	Lieutenant LT — Silver Bars	Captain Capt. — Silver Bars	Captain Capt. — Silver Bars
O4 Major MAJ — Gold Oak Leaf	Lieutenant Commander LCDR — Gold Oak Leaf	Major Maj. — Gold Oak Leaf	Major Maj. — Gold Oak Leaf

COMMISSIONED OFFICER RANK INSIGNIA *(Continued)*

ARMY	NAVY, CG NOAA, PHS	MARINE CORPS	AIR FORCE
O5	Commander CDR		
Lieutenant Colonel LTC		Lieutenant Colonel Lt. Col.	Lieutenant Colonel Lt. Col.
Silver Oak Leaf	Silver Leaf	Silver Oak Leaf	Silver Oak Leaf
O6	Captain CAPT		
Colonel COL		Colonel Col.	Colonel Col.
Silver Eagle	Silver Eagle	Silver Eagle	Silver Eagle
O7	Rear Admiral Lower Half RADM (LH)		
Brigadier General BG		Brigadier General Brig. Gen.	Brigadier General Brig. Gen.
Silver Star	Silver Star	Silver Star	Silver Star
O8	Rear Admiral Upper Half RADM (UH)		
Major General MG		Major General Maj. Gen.	Major General Maj. Gen.
Silver Stars	Silver Stars	Silver Stars	Silver Stars

COMMISSIONED OFFICER RANK INSIGNIA *(Continued)*

ARMY	NAVY, CG NOAA, PHS	MARINE CORPS	AIR FORCE
O9 Lieutenant General LTG ★★★ Silver Stars	Vice Admiral VADM ★★★ Silver Stars	Lieutenant General Lt. Gen. ★★★ Silver Stars	Lieutenant General Lt. Gen. ★★★ Silver Stars
O10 General GEN Army Chief of Staff ★★★★ Silver Stars	Admiral ADM Chief of Naval Operations and Commandant of the Coast Guard ★★★★ Silver Stars	General Gen. Commandant of the Marine Corps ★★★★ Silver Stars	General Gen. Air Force Chief of Staff ★★★★ Silver Stars
General of the Army (Reserved for wartime only) ★★★★★ Silver Stars	Fleet Admiral (Reserved for wartime only) ★★★★★ Silver Stars	(None)	General of the Air Force (Reserved for wartime only) ★★★★★ Silver

Source: U.S. Department of Defense Defenselink Website.

Appearance, Uniform, and Award Standards

Officers need to be cognizant of the importance of good grooming and compliance with uniform standards. The uniform is a key element in presenting a proper uniformed service image, coupled with a well groomed personal appearance. The following summary information highlights those features of personal grooming and uniform standards about which officers should be knowledgeable. For more detailed information, refer to official PHS Personnel Instructions and Directives.

PERSONAL APPEARANCE AND GROOMING
Source: Instruction CC412.01, 21 June 2013.

The primary consideration for PHS officers is that they present a professional appearance when in uniform. Grooming standards are based on several elements, including neatness, cleanliness, safety, image and appearance.

Hair, Cosmetics

Men. Hair shall be clean and neatly trimmed. Hair shall be no longer than four inches and may not touch the ears or shirt collar on the back, nor extend below the eyebrows. The bulk of hair may not exceed approximately two inches in depth. The hair shall not show under the front edge of headgear, nor interfere with properly wearing headgear. Sideburns shall not extend below a point level with the middle of the ear, shall be of even width (not flared), and end on a horizontal line. Hair coloring and hairpieces shall be natural in appearance. Male officers shall be clean shaven. A mustache is authorized, but must be neatly and closely trimmed, and not extend beyond the lip line of the upper lip. Cosmetics are not authorized for men. Fingernails shall be kept clean and not extend beyond the fingertips.

Women. Hair shall be clean, neat, and present a balanced and generally conservative appearance. The hair may touch, but not fall below a horizontal line level with the lower edge of the back of the shirt collar. The bulk of hair may not exceed approximately two inches in depth. Hair shall not show from under the front of headgear, nor interfere with the proper wearing of any headgear. Hair coloring and hairpieces or wigs shall be natural in appearance. A maximum of two small barrettes/combs/clips, similar to hair color, may be used in the hair. Additional bobby pins or rubber bands, similar to hair color, may be used to hold hair in place. Beads and hair decorations are not authorized. Women may apply cosmetics in good taste so that colors blend with natural skin tone and enhance natural features. Lipstick and nail polish may be worn, but colors shall be conservative and complement the skin tone. Fingernails shall be kept clean and not exceed ¼ inch, measured from the fingertips.

Body Alterations

No tattoos/body art/brands are permitted on the head, face, neck, scalp or exposed skin, and shall not be visible through or outside the uniform clothing. Individual tattoos/body art/brands exposed by wearing a short sleeve uniform shirt shall conform to size specifications in the Instruction. Tattoos are deemed unacceptable if visually offensive.

Articles, Communication Devices, Eyeglasses, Jewelry, Watches

When in uniform, *personal articles* such as pens, combs, and electronic *communication devices* shall not protrude from or be visible through the uniform. When a communication device is worn, it shall be conservative in color and design. With service or working uniforms, the device must be worn on either side of the hip, behind the elbow, so as not to be visible from the front; with a dress uniform, the device shall not be visible or bulging. Use of an earpiece, Bluetooth technology, headset or other hands-free device while in uniform is prohibited, unless authorized for official duties.

Eyeglasses, including sunglasses, must be conservative in design. Retainer straps are authorized for safety reasons only. If required, straps shall be plain, black, and worn snugly against the back of the head.

Jewelry, while in uniform, shall be conservative and in good taste, and not present a safety hazard. Only one ring per hand is authorized, plus a wedding/engagement ring set. Earrings are not authorized for men. Women may wear one gold earring per ear, 4mm-6mm, plain with shiny or brushed matte finish. Single white pearl earrings or diamond earrings of the same size are authorized with Dinner Dress or Service Dress uniforms. Only one necklace may be worn and it shall not be visible.

Only one conservative *wristwatch* and/or one *bracelet* may be worn on the same or different arms. Ankle bracelets are not authorized.

Bags

Bags (e.g., briefcase, gym bag, backpack, laptop bag, lunch bag, suitcase, garment bag) are carried in the left hand. Exceptions include the following: bags may be worn when riding a bicycle or motorcycle; bags may be worn on the left shoulder when wearing service or working uniforms; and, backpacks may be worn over both or either shoulder when wearing service or working uniforms. All bags must conceal their contents. Bags shall be black, navy blue or brown, except for the olive drab GI duffel bag. No ornamentation is allowed, except an official Corps logo in yellow or the bag manufacturer's logo (if small). Bags with logos of the Commissioned Officers Association of the USPHS, Association of Military Surgeons of the US, Society of American Military Engineers or the Reserve Officers Association may be carried only to their annual meetings. Women's handbags shall be carried over the left shoulder or forearm, placing the top of the handbag at waist level with all uniforms.

UNIFORM STANDARDS
Primary Sources: Instruction CC26.3.4/CC26.3.5, 02 February 2010; CC412.01, 21 June 2013.

The PHS uniform dates to 1873, when John Maynard Woodworth, the newly retitled Supervising Surgeon General of the Marine Hospital Service, adopted a military model for the Service's physicians, thereby forming a cadre of mobile, career service uniformed personnel. Today, the style of the uniform has evolved over the years, but continues to reflect the legacy and tradition of the more than 200 year old U.S Public Health Service.

There are specified standards regarding wear of the Commissioned Corps uniform. PHS and Navy uniforms are generally comprised of the same articles of clothing, with uniforms made distinctive by the unique PHS insignia, including the Corps device, cap chin strap, cap device, shoulder boards, and buttons. Similar to other services, PHS officers wear specific uniforms depending upon their assignment or the intended purpose of the uniform.

There are several categories of uniform, as follows.

General Purpose Service Uniforms
>   Service Dress Blue (SDB, Required)
>   Service Dress Blue Sweater
>   Service Dress White
>   Summer White (SW, Required)
>   Service Khaki

Working Uniforms
>   Blue Coverall Uniform
>   Operational Dress Uniform* (ODU, Required)

Special Purpose Uniforms
>   Battle Dress Uniform*
>   Maternity Uniform

Ceremonial Uniforms
>   Full Dress Blue
>   Full Dress White

Dinner Dress Uniforms**
>   Dinner Dress Blue Jacket
>   Dinner Dress White Jacket
>   Dinner Dress Blue
>   Dinner Dress White

* The BDU is replaced with the ODU, effective 01 January 2015.

**The Dinner Jacket versions are more formal than the regular versions, which use the Service Dress coat. The Jacket uniform is a prescribable uniform for O-4 and above, and optional for O-3 and below.

Uniform Policy

PHS officers are directed to wear the uniform daily while on official duty. PHS officers may wear only those uniforms designated Uniform of the Day that are prescribed by the Surgeon General, who is the National Uniform Authority, or by the Local Uniform Authority, as appropriate. Such uniform is selected from among the "General Purpose Service Uniforms." Additionally, Service Dress Blue is always acceptable in a normal office setting.

Assignment to Other Uniformed Service. PHS officers assigned to the U.S. Coast Guard for extended active duty wear the uniform prescribed for wear by Coast Guard officers, but with PHS shoulder boards, cap and Corps devices, sleeve insignia, and PHS buttons. PHS officers assigned to a uniformed service other than the Coast Guard for extended active duty shall, if required under the provisions of the assignment agreement, wear the uniform prescribed for that service. If the agreement does not specify that the officer is not to wear the PHS Corps uniform, or the uniform of the service to which assigned, the officer shall wear the PHS uniform that corresponds to the type of uniform prescribed for wear by officers of the other service.

Travel. For official travel on non-military conveyances within the United States, an officer may wear the uniform specified in orders, Service Dress Blue, or appropriate civilian attire. For official travel outside the U.S., appropriate civilian attire will normally be worn. For official and unofficial travel by military-owned or -controlled conveyance, PHS officers are authorized to wear civilian clothing, or, may wear the PHS uniform for military travel, with some exceptions. The officer shall wear the uniform when travelers belonging to the uniformed service that is providing the conveyance are required to travel in uniform, or when the officer in charge of a group of Corps officers traveling together, so specifies. The officer shall *not* wear the uniform when military officials advise that foreign entry requirements prohibit wearing the uniform, or when military officials or the U.S. Department of State advise that the traveler will be passing through high-risk areas relating to terrorist activities, or political or social unrest. For international travel, in accordance with international agreements, PHS officers are generally not permitted to wear the uniform outside the U.S. unless the Surgeon General gives authorization or the officer is assigned to another uniformed service whose regulations permit wearing the uniform.

Retired/Reserve Corps Officers. Retired and Reserve Corps officers not on active duty may wear the prescribed uniform of the rank held on the retired or ready reserve/inactive list on occasions of ceremony, military funerals, memorial services, weddings and inaugurals; at patriotic parades or ceremonies in which an active or reserve U.S. uniformed service is taking part; and, at meetings of associations or organizations comprised primarily of uniformed service members.

Uniform Considerations

Officers serve as role models and are expected to maintain the highest standards when wearing the uniform. Each uniform needs to be tailored to fit properly, maintained in good condition and replaced whenever necessary. Keep uniforms clean and pressed (military shirt creases recommended), and shoes shined and in good repair. Fabric badges, insignia and ribbons are to be clean and, if frayed, replaced. Metallic devices such as the belt buckle are to be clean and bright, and replaced if scratched. The gig line – the shirt placket, belt buckle, and trouser fly – are properly kept in vertical alignment.

Headgear

There are five principal types of headgear prescribed for PHS officers.

The *combination cap* is the standard officer's cap covered in white or khaki material, as appropriate, with black visor and distinctive device and ornamentation. The combination cap is worn squarely on the head, with the bottom edge parallel to the ground and approximately 1½ inches above the eyebrows. The cap is worn so that hair does not show on the forehead.

The *garrison cap* is made of khaki material. The garrison cap is worn squarely on the head, with the fore and aft crease centered vertically between the eyebrows, and with the lowest point of the cap approximately 1 inch above the eyebrows. The cap is worn so that hair is not visible below the front of the cover. When stowed on the hip, the garrison cap is placed under the belt in front of the belt loop on either side pant pocket, with opening to the rear.

The *beret*, authorized for female officers only, is a black, semi-rigid, feminine style beret. The beret is worn toward the front of the head, approximately ¾ inch from the forehead hairline, and tilted slightly to the right.

Two *command ball caps* are authorized: black (worn with the BDU), and blue (worn with the ODU), with U.S. PUBLIC HEALTH SERVICE embroidered using ½ inch high, upper case letters in an arch across the top front panel. The cap is worn squarely on the head, with the bottom edge parallel to the ground and about 1½ inches above the eyebrows.

The 8-point *utility cap* is Woodland (for BDU), and blue (for ODU), Navy style cap with eight sides and firm bill, plaited sides and a high front panel. The cap is worn squarely on the head, with the bottom edge parallel to the ground and approximately 1½ inches above the eyebrows.

Name Tag

The PHS name tag is a required component of the service uniforms; it is not worn with ceremonial or dinner dress uniforms. The name tag is inscribed with the officer's last name only. Officers must own regular Corps name tags with the PHS seal. Name tags with approved organization-specific designations may also be worn. The name tag is positioned on the right side, with the lower edge of the tag centered ¼ inch above the breast pocket or flap or, absent a pocket, above the same relative position as the left breast pocket.

Insignia

Cap. The *combination cap* has the standard size PHS cap device, which is centered on the front of the black hat band, with a chin strap, and visor (male officer) or hat band (female officer) with ornamentation, as appropriate for rank: o-4 and below, no ornamentation; o-6 and o-5, the male officer's visor and female officer's hat band is embroidered with one row of gold oak leaves and acorns; flag officer, the male officer's visor and female officer's hat band is fully embroidered with two rows of gold oak leaves and acorns.

The *garrison cap* has the miniature metal rank insignia on the right side and the miniature PHS cap device on the left. The devices are centered 1½ inches from the lower edge, and 2 inches from the front center line crease of the cap. For Captain/o-6 rank insignia, wear the right eagle (i.e., eagle's head points toward the front center crease).

The *beret* has the miniature PHS cap device positioned so as to be aligned over the left eye; no rank insignia is worn on the beret.

The *command ball cap* has, centered underneath U.S. PUBLIC HEALTH SERVICE: black cap – the large bright metal rank device insignia; blue cap – the large bright direct embroidered rank insignia. For o-6 rank insignia, the eagle faces to the wearer's right. Visor ornamentation appropriate for rank, in the style of the combination cap, is authorized for ranks o-5 and above.

The *utility cap* has the metal pin-on large bright rank insignia centered on the front panel (for o-6 rank insignia, the eagle faces to the wearer's right). There is no PHS cap device and no visor ornamentation for rank.

Collar. Miniature metal rank insignia are worn on the right collar points of open collar khaki shirt. The center of the rank insignia is 1 inch from the front and lower edge of the collar, and positioned on the vertical axis of the insignia along an imaginary line bisecting the angle of the collar point. For flag officers, a single star is worn with one ray pointing toward the neck, with additional stars positioned such that a horizontal line through the stars is perpendicular to the line bisecting the angle of the collar points. A miniature metal PHS Corps device is worn on the left collar, centered 1 inch from the appropriate collar edges, as described above; the staff of the caduceus is the vertical axis of the device and the anchor points toward the front.

Shoulder. Hard shoulder boards (HSB) consist of a PHS Corps device, appropriate rank stripe, and PHS gilt button. Female HSBs are approximately ½ inch shorter than the male HSB. The HSB is positioned with the square end facing outboard at the shoulder seam and the gilt button facing inboard toward the neck. The anchor of the Corps device points forward (hence the saying, "don't drag your anchors") when the boards are worn on the correct shoulder. Soft shoulder boards (SSM) are similar in design to the HSBs, without the gilt button. SSMs are made to ¾ scale of the men's HSB for both male and female officers.

AWARD, RIBBON/MEDAL STANDARDS

Awards and Decorations

Awards and decorations are awarded to uniformed service members to recognize exceptional merit, including performance of duties and specific acts or achievements that are particularly noteworthy. These awards are represented by medals and ribbons worn on an officer's uniform. The placement and order of precedence is prescribed for all awards, including those received by PHS officers while serving in other uniformed services.

Order of Precedence. PHS Corps and uniformed service awards and decorations are arranged in the following order of precedence:

PHS Corps, Uniformed Service Individual Honor Awards/Decorations
PHS Corps, Uniformed Service Unit Awards
Non-Uniformed Service Decorations
PHS Corps Campaign and Service Awards
Uniformed Service Campaign and Service Awards*
PHS Regular Corps Ribbon and Training Awards
Foreign Military Decorations and Non-U.S. Service Awards*
Foreign Military Unit Awards*
Non-U.S. Service Awards*
Foreign Military Service Awards*
Marksmanship Ribbons
Association and Organization Awards
* See Instruction CC26.3.3, 28 August 2008 for these lists.

Listed below, in order of precedence, are awards and decorations which are authorized for wear on the PHS Corps uniform.

Individual Honor Awards and Decorations

The order of precedence is as follows.

Medal of Honor
Army Distinguished Service Cross
Navy, Air Force, Coast Guard Cross
Defense Distinguished Service Medal
Homeland Security Distinguished Service Medal
Distinguished Service Medal (PHS)
Distinguished Service Medal (Other Services)
Silver Star
Dept. of Transportation* (DOT) Secretary's Award for
    Outstanding Achievement/ DOT Gold Medal (USCG)
Commerce Gold Medal (NOAA)
Defense Superior Service Medal
Commerce Silver Medal (NOAA)
Legion of Merit
Distinguished Flying Cross
Soldier's Medal (Army)
Navy and Marine Corps Medal
Airman's Medal (Air Force)
Coast Guard Medal

Gold Lifesaving Medal (USCG)
Bronze Star
Purple Heart
Meritorious Service Medal (PHS)
Defense Meritorious Service Medal
Meritorious Service Medal (Other Services)
Surgeon General's Medallion (PHS)
Surgeon General's Exemplary Service Medal (PHS)
Commerce Bronze Medal (NOAA)
Air Medal
Outstanding Service Medal (PHS)
NOAA Administrator's Award
Silver Lifesaving Medal (USCG)
DOT* Secretary's Award for Meritorious
    Achievement/DOT Silver Medal (USCG)
Aerial Achievement Medal
Commendation Medal (PHS)
Joint Service Commendation Medal
Commendation Medal (Other Services)
DOT* Award for Superior
    Achievement/DOT Bronze Medal (USCG)
Achievement Medal (PHS)
Joint Service Achievement Medal
Achievement Medal (Other Services)
Commerce Special Achievement Medal (NOAA)
PHS Citation
Commandant's Letter of Commendation Ribbon
NOAA Corps Director's Award
Combat Action Ribbon (Navy, USMC, USCG)
Air Force Combat Action Medal
* *Upon transfer of the US Coast Guard to the Department of Homeland Security in 2003, DOT awards to the USCG were discontinued.*

Unit Awards

The order of precedence is as follows.

Presidential Unit Citation (All Services)
Joint Meritorious Unit Award
Outstanding Unit Citation (PHS)
DOT* Outstanding Unit Award (USCG)
Army Valorous Unit Award
Unit Commendation (PHS)
Unit Commendation Ribbon (All Services)
Meritorious Unit Commendation (All Services)
Army Superior Unit Award
Air Force Outstanding Unit Award
Coast Guard Meritorious Team Commendation
Navy "E" Ribbon,   Coast Guard "E" Ribbon
Air Force Organizational Excellence Award
* *Upon transfer of the US Coast Guard to the Department of Homeland Security in 2003, DOT awards to the USCG were discontinued.*

Non-Uniformed Service Decorations

At least one uniformed service award must be worn at the same time. The order of precedence is as follows.

Presidential Medal of Freedom
Presidential Citizens Medal
National Security Medal
National Sciences Medal
Medal for Merit
President's Distinguished Federal Civilian Service Medal
National Intelligence Distinguished Service Medal
National Intelligence Medal of Achievement
Department of Defense Distinguished Civilian Service Award
Secretary of Defense Civilian Meritorious Service Award
Bureau of Prisons (BOP) Distinguished Service Medal
BOP Meritorious Service Medal
BOP Commendation Medal
Environmental Protection Agency (EPA) Gold Medal
EPA Silver Medal
EPA Bronze Medal
EPA Distinguished Career Award
* See Instruction CC26.3.3, 28 August 2008 for remainder of this list.

PHS Corps Campaign and Service Awards

The order of precedence is as follows.

Smallpox Eradication Campaign Ribbon
Global Health Campaign Medal
Hazardous Duty Award
Foreign Duty Award
Special Assignment Award
Isolated/Hardship Award
Crisis Response Service Award
Global Response Service Award
Response Service Award
National Emergency Preparedness Award
Recruitment Service Ribbon
Global Health Initiative Service Medal
Bicentennial Unit Commendation

See Instruction CC26.3.3, 28 August 2008, for the following listings.

Uniformed Service Campaign and Service Awards

PHS Regular Corps Ribbon and Training Awards

Uniformed Service Training Awards

Foreign Decorations and Non-U.S. Service Awards

Foreign Unit Awards

Non-U.S. Service Awards

Foreign Military Service Awards

Marksmanship Ribbons

Association and Organization Awards

These medals/ribbons are not authorized for routine daily wear. They may only be worn while in attendance at meetings or other events as a member of these organizations. The order of precedence is as follows.
Commissioned Officers Association of the USPHS, Inc.
Association of Military Surgeons of the United States
Reserve Officers Association
Society of American Military Engineers

Ribbons/Medals

Ribbons. Ribbons are arranged in the order of precedence in rows from the top down, and inboard to outboard within rows. Ribbons are worn in horizontal rows of three each. If not in multiples of three ribbons, the top row contains the lesser number, with the center of this row located over the center of the row below it. The lower edge of the bottom row is centered ¼ inch above the left breast pocket. When the uppermost ribbons are covered by the coat lapel, the uppermost rows may contain two ribbons each, and aligned with the left border of the rack. All ribbons may be worn, if desired. A minimum of three ribbons are worn by those officers with three or more; if only one row of ribbons is worn, it shall consist of the three senior ribbons.

Large Medals. Large medals are worn on Full Dress uniforms, suspended from a holding bar. Medals are arranged in the order of precedence in rows from the top down, and inboard to outboard within rows. Medals are worn in horizontal rows of three medals side by side, or up to five medals overlapping. Overlapping shall be equal, with the right or inboard medal showing in full. If not in equal multiples, all rows except the top row consist of equal numbers of medals and the top row consists of the lesser number of medals. Upper rows of medals are mounted so that these medals cover the suspension ribbons of the medals below. The lower edge of the bottom holding bar is centered ¼ inch above the left breast pocket. All medals may be worn. A minimum of five medals are worn by those officers with five or more; if only one row of medals is worn, it shall consist of the five senior medals.

Miniature Medals. Miniature medals are worn with all Formal Dress uniforms and Dinner Dress uniforms, suspended from a holding bar. Medals are arranged in the order of precedence in rows from the top down, and inboard to outboard within rows. Medals are worn in horizontal rows of three to five medals side by side with no overlap. If not in equal multiples, all rows except the top row consist of equal numbers of medals and the top row consists of the lesser number of medals. Upper rows of medals are mounted so that these medals cover the suspension ribbons of the medals below. For Service Dress Blue or White coats, the lower edge of the bottom holding bar is centered ¼ inch above the left breast pocket. For the male officer's Dinner Dress Jacket, the holding bar of the bottom row is positioned 3 inches below the notch and centered on the lapel; three or more miniature medals are positioned starting at the inner edge of the lapel. For the female officer's Dinner Dress uniform, the holding bar is worn in the same relative position as on the male's Dinner Dress Jacket, down one-third of the distance from the shoulder seam to the coat hem. All medals may be worn. If only one row of medals is worn, it shall consist of the five senior medals.

Ribbon and Medal Stars. Medal stars are worn on ribbons and medals in lieu of a second or subsequent of the same award. One or more stars are positioned in the center of the ribbon bar or the suspension ribbon of medals. Stars are placed on the ribbon with one ray pointing up. When medals overlap, all stars may be positioned to the wearer's left.

For PHS Honor Awards, a 5/16" gold star is worn in lieu of a second or subsequent like award, and a 5/16" silver star is worn in lieu of five gold stars, on the ribbon bars and the suspension ribbon of large medals. For miniature medals, the star is 1/8" in size.

For PHS Unit and Service Awards, a 3/16" bronze star is worn in lieu of a second or subsequent like award, and a 3/16" silver star is worn in lieu of five bronze stars.

Surgeon General's Medallion. When either large or miniature medals are prescribed, the Surgeon General's Medallion is worn from its suspension ribbon placed around the neck. When worn with the White Service coat, the ribbon shall pass outside the coat collar; when worn with all other coats, the ribbon shall pass between the shirt and coat collar.

Badges
Source: PPM 08-019, 28 August 2008.

The following badges and their placement on uniforms are authorized.

- U.S. Surgeon General, Deputy Surgeon General, Officer in Charge, and Chief Professional Officer badges, full size, are placed on the right side of the uniform, centered below the PHS name tag; female officers may use that location or relocate the badge above the name tag. Such badges are only worn while an incumbent of the position, noting that these badges are not authorized for officers in an acting or temporary position. Following completion of the tour of duty, the miniature badge is worn on the officer's right side, centered above the name tag.

- PHS Recruiter, Associate Recruiter Lead (ARL), and Associate Recruiter (AR) badges are placed on the left side of the uniform, centered below the service ribbons in the left pocket area; female officers may use that location or relocate the badge above the name tag. When worn with a shirt as part of a service uniform, the ARL or AR badge may be suspended from the left pocket button by a plastic fob. The badges are placed on the right side below the PHS name tag when worn with a ceremonial uniform. These badges are worn only while the officer has responsibility for, or association with, PHS Corps recruitment programs.

- Field Medical Readiness Badge (FMRB) is worn on the left side of the uniform, centered above the left pocket or the service ribbons.

- Office of the Secretary, HHS Identification (HHS ID) miniature badge is worn by male officers on summer white and service khaki uniforms centered on the left pocket below the pocket flap, and the full sized HHS ID badge is worn on service dress blue and service dress white uniforms centered below the left pocket tab or below the lowest row of full sized medals. For female officers, the HHS ID badge, regardless of size, is worn centered above the left pocket or above the ribbons. For dinner dress uniforms, both male and female officers wear the miniature HHS ID badge below the lowest row of miniature medals.

- Authorized identification or skill badges earned in another uniformed service are centered on the left pocket below the pocket flap, and female officers may wear the badge in this location or may relocate the badge above the left pocket or ribbons. If a PHS ID badge is already in this location, the non-PHS badge may be relocated on the right side. Skill badges earned in other uniformed services are worn on the left side, centered above the left pocket or ribbons.

Aiguillette
Source: PPM 10-002, 04 December 2009.

Individuals may wear an aiguillette only while serving in an official capacity during specific events in which wearing the aiguillette, as an identifying device, is important to the principal being aided. Such identification enables the principal to accomplish his/her mission more effectively. Aiguillettes are furnished by the staff requiring them and remain in their custody. Aiguillettes are normally worn on the left shoulder; however, they are worn on the right shoulder when serving as an Aide to the President, Vice President, at the White House, and designated aides to foreign heads of state.

PHS aiguillettes are of the same style as those utilized by the U.S. Navy. Service aiguillettes consist of a number of loops of aiguillette cord covered with gold or gilt and other colored thread, with dark blue thread woven to form spiral bands. The number of loops has a hierarchical correspondence: four gold loops, aide to the President; four gold loops with blue bands, aide to the Vice President, Admiral, Cabinet Secretary/Deputy Secretary, White House, or foreign heads of state; three gold loops with blue bands, aide to vice admiral or lieutenant general; two loops with blue bands, aide to rear admiral, major general, brigadier general, Assistant Secretary, or State/Territorial Governor. If the Assistant Secretary for Health is a Corps officer, the aide shall wear a service aiguillette with four gold loops and blue bands.

CHAPTER TWO

LEADERSHIP PRINCIPLES

There is an expectation that uniformed service officers show leadership in all endeavors. Therefore, uniformed service personnel attain through didactic and experiential learning the attributes needed to effectively interact with and lead others, and successfully accomplish the stated mission. This chapter provides an overview of officership and the principles of leadership in the USPHS.

> USPHS CORE VALUES
> OFFICERSHIP
> LEADERSHIP THEORY
> LEADERSHIP COMPETENCIES
> LEADERSHIP PRINCIPLES
> PHS LEADERSHIP COMPETENCY MODEL

USPHS Core Values

Every uniformed service has a set of core values that are unique to the Service. Core values form the foundation of the corporate culture, and are essential for the credibility and sustained viability of a uniformed service in its operations and management. Core values provide guidance with respect to how officers are to conduct themselves and perform their duties in accomplishing the *USPHS Mission* of protecting, promoting, and advancing the health and safety of our Nation (see pages 3 and 152). Proudly adopt and adhere to the following USPHS Core Values as integral to your duty and professional life:

Leadership Provides vision and purpose in public health through inspiration, dedication, and loyalty.

Service Demonstrates a commitment to public health through compassionate actions and stewardship of time, resources, and talents.

Integrity Exemplifies uncompromising ethical conduct and maintains the highest standards of responsibility and accountability.

Excellence Exhibits superior performance and continuous improvement in knowledge and expertise.

Officership

The USPHS Oath of Office is the same as that taken by personnel of all other uniformed services, as follows:

> "I, (name), do solemnly swear (*or* affirm) that I will support and defend the Constitution of the United States against all enemies, foreign and domestic; that I will bear true faith and allegiance to the same; that I take this obligation freely without any mental reservation or purpose of evasion; and that I will well and faithfully discharge the duties of the office on which I am about to enter, so help me God."

The Oath of Office confers upon individuals the special recognition of being both a *professional officer* and a *health care/public health professional*, with an inherent obligation of honorable service to the Nation.

PHS officers have very fulfilling work in administrative, clinical, regulatory and scientific positions. They distinguish themselves by their public health mission and array of responsibilities – they are leaders in health care delivery and education, biomedical research, disease control, environmental health, public health management and regulatory protection, increasingly on a global scale. Although the roles may differ, the commonality of purpose – to protect, promote, and advance the health and safety of our Nation – is a unifying force. Certain personal and leadership qualities are important in a commissioned officer, referred to as the qualities of officership. Although there is no universal definition, **officership** can generally be described as

> *the essence of being an officer* – an expectation that all officers are leaders, use professional judgment, have ethical values that instill trust, and understand the relationship of the Corps and its role in service to society.

For PHS officers, characteristics of officership include the following.

- *Professional competence,* both as a specialist in a particular discipline and an officer. The PHS officer is a member of his/her chosen profession, usually a health-related field, and becomes a professional officer after incorporating personal and organizational values of the PHS.
- *Public health professional.* The PHS officer is at first a competent specialist in a profession. Yet, the officer attains a broader understanding of public health principles through job positions, didactic and field training to also become a competent leader who is able to contribute to public health initiatives and respond to public health emergencies.
- *Adherence to core values.* Throughout their careers, officers are challenged with supporting the PHS mission while conforming to those enduring values that guide and sustain both the individual and organization.
- *Ability as a manager and leader.* PHS officers broaden their capabilities throughout their career, often accompanied by higher levels of responsibility. All officers are expected to be leaders, and must be proactive in obtaining leadership training to meet Corps expectations.

- *Mission accomplishment.* Accomplishment of mission is a hallmark of the uniformed services. The basis for this relates to the fact that there is no option to fail in armed conflict (to do so could place the Nation in peril). Nonetheless, it applies to all responsibilities and tasks undertaken by uniformed service personnel. Mission accomplishment infers the completion of duties on time, while meeting high performance and quality standards.

All five aspects of officership are important. Some indicators of officership that express the professionalism of being a USPHS commissioned officer include competence in your profession and assigned billet; demonstration of one's capabilities as a public health leader; mentoring; professional partnering; teaching; serving on deployments; participation on Corps-related committees and task groups; and, professional presentations and publications in journals.

Attitude and Actions. Officership requires that commissioned officers always be cognizant of their attitudes and actions, and their interactive relationships with colleagues. Commissioned officers have a responsibility to conduct themselves appropriately. Appropriate conduct relates to one's attitude and actions – it is conveyed by an officer's mind-set in performing his duties and how the officer relates to other uniformed service personnel, government officials and the public. Although officership relates primarily to one's service, the responsibility of appropriate conduct extends, as well, to non-duty life. By electing to become a member of a uniformed service, PHS officers accept that they are part of a hierarchical structure with certain prescribed features. They agree to conform to the conventions of uniformed service protocol and observe uniformed service behavior and courtesies. When in uniform, officers are expected to practice discipline in managing their personal feelings in order to place service before self. The "uniformed service way" is to approach each challenge with a positive, can-do attitude followed by action to accomplish the mission, whether that mission involves an order given on the battlefield or a routine assignment in the office. PHS officers complete their mission by performance of duty with excellence, bottom line.

Teamwork. The nature of a uniformed service is such that it is operationally best and most successful when a teamwork approach is used. Therefore, service personnel must be respectful of one another, cooperate with others and work together for the common good, keeping foremost in mind the overall mission. With mission in mind, good officers will stand ready to help other officers succeed in their respective duty roles.

Personal ambition and competition are appropriate when an officer or group of officers is striving for excellence – the officer and service can benefit from such effort. However, personal ambition has no place in a uniformed service if it is unethical or injurious to others. Officers must make a conscious effort to think how their actions affect others and adjust their actions and motivations, accordingly. Selfless service undergirds all uniformed service.

Leadership Theory

The characteristics of officership include several qualities, but chief among these is leadership. Effective leadership is key to ensuring that personnel are fulfilled in their roles, that teamwork flourishes, and a quality outcome is attained. Commissioned officers are called upon to be leaders in every way. PHS officers need to understand the importance of good leadership ability and seek leadership training early in their career. There are many definitions of leadership. Generally stated:

> **Leadership** *is the ability to influence others by strength of character and personal vision to achieve common goals.*

Military officers are taught to be leaders. The reason is evident – the military exists to defend and protect our Nation, and that entails fighting wars. When going into battle, losing is not an option, and military officers must courageously lead soldiers into battle for the common good. Although not all military personnel serve in combat, all military people take their responsibilities seriously in support of the mission, and share a unity of purpose that places great emphasis on duty, honor, and Country.

PHS officers, though not an armed force, share a common purpose with other uniformed services in supporting the welfare of our Nation. In meeting their responsibilities, PHS officers are leaders by carrying out their duties with integrity, by keeping their focus on service to others before self, and by taking initiative to make the world a better place.

FOUNDATIONAL THEORIES

There have been numerous leadership theories advanced over the period of about a hundred years that provide a foundation for newer, present day narratives about what constitutes good leadership. Although each of these foundational theories cannot stand solely as the basis of leadership, each has certain elements that remain important in describing desired leadership qualities. The following are brief descriptions of some of the more predominant theories.

- *Trait Theory.* Defines a leadership profile in terms of distinguishing personal traits, such as competence, courage, intelligence, trustworthiness. Certain core personality traits may be predictors of leadership effectiveness, particularly when considered within the situational context.

- *Behavioral Theory.* Relies on observations of leadership behavior and leadership styles. The main styles include directive leadership, whereby a leader provides guidance and work expectations to subordinates, and which is closely aligned with a production-centered concern to achieve specific objectives; and participative leadership, whereby decision-making is a shared endeavor and is aligned with a people-centered concern for the needs and interests of followers or subordinates.

- *Situational Theory.* Notes that effective leadership is contingent upon and influenced by the context of a situation, and the leader will adapt and use an approach that is appropriate to the surrounding environment or state of events, the person or group that is being influenced, and/or the task or function that needs to be accomplished.

- *Servant Theory.* The leader places the needs and concerns of subordinate staff who report to and work with him/her over their own self-interest.

- *Transformational Theory.* The leader is a charismatic, strategic visionary who inspires, challenges and motivates others for change, and is supportive of followers in reaching their full potential.

Each of these theories can provide the PHS officer with useful conceptual approaches to consider when forming a personalized approach to leadership, and all provide insight into useful attributes and skills development. Leadership theories continue to evolve, with current theories complexly interwoven, taking into account factors such as the relationship of leaders and followers, the exercise of authority, the impact of differing organizational context and culture, and further delineation of transformative leadership.

MANAGEMENT AND LEADERSHIP

Managers and Leaders. A comparative review of the tasks and skill sets associated with managerial and leadership roles provides insight with respect to the distinguishing features of each role. Leadership and management functions in an organization are both important and complementary, but they are different. The *manager's role* is to plan, budget, staff, implement and oversee the operational aspects of an endeavor, to problem-solve, and ensure that there is a successful outcome or end product. The *leader's role* is to provide an organizational direction and vision, and to inspire and motivate followers to embrace positive change. The prominent business scholar Peter Drucker put it more succinctly: "Management is doing things right; leadership is doing the right things." The two roles are not mutually exclusive, because of possible overlap due to the fact that we work in multifaceted organizational environments and deal with increasingly complex issues. Further, individuals may necessarily perform elements of both leader and manager.

Desirable Managerial Traits. As reported by R. Beck and J. Harter in the *Harvard Blog Network* in March 2014, the Gallup company researched worker performance at hundreds of organizations and measured the engagement of 27 million employees and more than 2.5 million work units for over two decades. Gallup discovered links between employee engagement at the business unit level and vital performance indicators. When the organization raises employee engagement levels consistently across every business unit, everything improves. To make this happen, however, companies need great managers, and Gallup found that great managers have the following talents.

- They **motivate** every single employee to take action and engage them with a compelling mission and vision.
- They have the **assertiveness** to drive outcomes and the ability to overcome adversity and resistance.
- They create a culture of clear **accountability**.
- They build **relationships** that create trust, open dialogue, and full transparency.
- They make **decisions** that are based on productivity, not politics.

Gallup's research reveals that only about one in ten people have all these necessary traits. These 10%, when put in managerial roles, engage team members, retain top performers, and sustain a culture of high productivity.

Transactional and Transformational Leadership. This paradigm of transactional and transformational leadership, introduced by James MacGregor Burns and others, has some relation to the distinction between manager and leader. The concept of *transactional leadership*, also known as managerial leadership, uses an "exchange" model, where the leader provides subordinates with tangible rewards that are contingent upon the achievement of set goals (e.g., meeting quality and performance standards), and penalizing (e.g., corrective action) noncompliance. Transactional leaders are generally directive, and focused on processes and productivity. Such leaders are most effective in completing projects with specific requirements and in emergency situations.

Transformational leadership describes a leader who is a trusted individual with the ability to articulate a creative, yet challenging vision, and motivate and inspire followers to take ownership of their contribution toward realizing that common goal. The transformational leader is often involved with effecting substantive organizational change and, in the process, ennobles and transforms followers with a meaningful purpose and desire to achieve.

Emotional Intelligence

It is believed that effective leaders have a high level of *emotional intelligence,* or *EI*, and a related attribute termed *social intelligence*. The EI concept gained popularity with the publication of *Emotional Intelligence – Why It Can Matter More Than IQ*, by David Goleman. The concept, in essence, refers to five skills that enable leaders to recognize and understand how their own emotions affect themselves and others; and, how to regulate emotions in themselves and others to improve relationships and enhance performance. They include:

- Self-awareness. Knowing one's emotions, strengths, weaknesses, drives, values and goals, and their impact on others.
- Self-regulation. Controlling/redirecting disruptive emotions and impulses.
- Motivation. Being driven to achieve for the sake of achievement.
- Empathy. Considering others' feelings and emotional makeup.
- Social skill. Building rapport with others.

It is postulated that through careful listening, observation of others and practice, these abilities will be strengthened and will be manifest in more self-confidence, integrity, a passion for challenging work, cross-cultural sensitivity, ability to develop and lead others, and greater effectiveness in leading change.

Level 5 Leadership

In *Level 5 Leadership: The Triumph of Humility and Fierce Resolve* (Harvard Business Review), by Jim Collins, research provides the basis for identifying unique factors and variables that differentiate good and great companies. Of the seven factors Collins identified as essential to take such an organization from good to great, with sustained superlative performance, the quality and nature of leadership was deemed most significant.

The term "Level 5 leadership" is used to describe the common leadership characteristic that is a necessary requirement for transforming an organization from good to great. This type of leadership forms the top level of a 5-level hierarchy that ranges from competent supervision to strategic executive decision-making. Further study of the behaviors and attitudes of the Level 5 leaders indicate that many display an unusual mix of intense determination, professional will, and profound personal humility. Such leaders often have a long-term personal sense of investment in people and the company and its success, often fostered through a career climb up the company's ranks. Executives who have this paradoxical combination of traits are catalysts for the statistically rare event of transforming a good organization into a great one.

"Level 5" refers to the highest level in a hierarchy of executive capabilities identified during the research. Leaders at the other four levels in the hierarchy are appropriate in their own right and can produce high degrees of success, but not enough to elevate organizations from mediocrity to sustained excellence. Individuals do not need to proceed sequentially through each level of the hierarchy to reach the top, but to be a Level 5 leader requires the capabilities of all the lower levels, plus the special characteristics of Level 5. Herewith are the five Levels.

- Level 5, Executive. Builds enduring greatness through a paradoxical combination of personal humility plus professional will.
- Level 4, Effective leader. Catalyzes commitment to and vigorous pursuit of a clear and compelling vision; stimulates the group to high performance standards.
- Level 3, Competent manager. Organizes people and resources toward the effective and efficient pursuit of predetermined objectives.
- Level 2, Contributing team member. Contributes to the achievement of group objectives; works effectively with others in a group setting.
- Level 1, Highly capable individual. Makes productive contributions through talent, knowledge, skills, and good work habits.

The Level 5 leader displays an unwavering resolve and sets the standard of building an enduring great organization. Collins presents some disciplines that other leaders can employ to grow into Level 5 leaders. Attend to people first, strategy second. Bring the right people on board and prepare a strategy. Deal with the facts of the current reality, while maintaining absolute faith that you will prevail (the "Stockdale [Admiral, USN] paradox"). Keep pushing the organizational "flywheel" with consistent effort, and the momentum will increase until the wheel hits the breakthrough point. And, think of the company as three intersecting circles: what it can be best at, how its economics work best, and what heightens its people's passions; then, eliminate everything else.

5 Levels of Leadership

In *The 5 Levels of Leadership*, by John C. Maxwell, the concept suggests that a person needs to master the ability to invest in and inspire people to build a productive team. In so doing, the leader will undergo a five-stage process of progressive growth and transformation into an authentic leader.

- Level 1, Position. The starting place for every leader is simply to have a *position* of leadership. Positional leadership is based on the rights granted by the position and title. The position itself, however, does not bestow leadership ability, and staff people generally only follow within the boundaries of the incumbent's authority and company policies.

- Level 2, Permission. The people follow the leader because they want to, based upon mutual trust. A leader at this level must be self-aware, honestly learning his/her strengths and weaknesses, and taking self-responsibility. The leader focuses more on people, and is getting to know and like his people; and, followers are learning about their leader, and lasting relationships are being built.

- Level 3, Production. On this level, leaders gain credibility and people follow them because of what they have done for the organization. Work gets done well and on time, morale improves, and goals are achieved. Leaders can become change agents, and are able to influence and take their people to a higher level of effectiveness.

- Level 4, People Development. At this level, leaders use their position, relationships and productivity to empower others, and invest in their people to become leaders in their own right. Performance increases and loyalty is strengthened.

- Level 5, Pinnacle. Leaders not only require intentionality, effort and skill, but also a high amount of talent to reach this level. Such leaders develop and mentor others to become leaders, and create their organization into a high performance entity. The leaders gain an exemplary reputation for leading the organization with integrity and vision.

Five Practices of Exemplary Leadership

The Leadership Challenge, by Kouzes and Posner, had its origins in research that began in 1983 to determine the leadership competencies that are essential to getting extraordinary things done in organizations. They learned what people did when they were at their "personal best" in leading others. The research was the basis of a leadership model called The Five Practices of Exemplary Leadership and a quantitative instrument – the Leadership Practices Inventory (LPI) – to measure those leadership practices. Today, LPI is among the more widely used leadership assessment tools. The following Five Practices and Ten Commitments reflect the study findings when leaders are at their best.

- Model the Way
  - *Clarify values by finding your voice and affirming shared values.*
  - *Set the example by aligning actions with shared values.*
    Leaders must discover a set of principles that guide decisions and actions. They understand and appreciate the values of others and affirm shared values. Leaders show others by their actions that they live by the values they profess.

- Inspire a Shared Vision
  - *Envision the future by imagining exciting and ennobling possibilities.*
  - *Enlist others in a common vision by appealing to shared aspirations.*
    Leaders envision a future of what can be, and have a sense of what is possible if everyone works together for a common purpose. They communicate their vision so that others clearly understand and share them as their own.

- Challenge the Process
  - *Search for opportunities by seizing the initiative and looking outward for innovative ways to improve.*
  - *Experiment and take risks by constantly generating small wins and learning from experience.*
    Leaders seek challenging opportunities and make something meaningful happen. They look for good ideas everywhere and promote external communication. They move forward incrementally with small victories, and turn adversity into advantage. They take bold risks and accept setbacks as learning opportunities.

- Enable Others to Act
  - *Foster collaboration by building trust and facilitating relationships.*
  - *Strengthen others by increasing self-determination and developing competence.*
    Leaders foster collaboration and cooperative relationships with colleagues. Mutual respect is what sustains extraordinary group efforts. They make others feel strong, capable, and confident to take both initiative and responsibility.

- Encourage the Heart
  - *Recognize contributions by showing appreciation for individual excellence.*
  - *Celebrate the values and victories by creating a spirit of community.*
    Leaders give heart by recognizing people's contributions to the common vision. They celebrate team accomplishments. They make people feel like heroes.

Leadership Competencies

Throughout one's career in the Public Health Service, officers need to be attentive to showing good leadership while developing their core competencies. Depending on where an officer is within his/her career, some competencies may be emphasized more than others, and perhaps at different levels of significance. Lifelong learning and enhancement of leader competencies is imperative to success in the Commissioned Corps. In addition to learning leadership skill sets, practical application of that knowledge is essential. Officers are only leaders if others perceive them to be. Officers show leadership through actions that exemplify a good leader. For example, good officers take initiative to lead a group effort, seek solutions to challenging situations, and provide strategic vision for their program.

OPM Core Qualifications

Most leadership training focuses on the development of skills and abilities, which are combined with a self-awareness of personal attributes, experiences, and external influences. The Federal Office of Personnel Management (OPM) Senior Executive Service has identified five **Executive Core Qualifications** (ECQs) to describe the critical leadership skills needed to succeed. Competencies are the personal and professional attributes that are critical to successful performance. There are twenty-two competencies that are specific to the Core Qualifications. The following abridged excerpts are illustrative.

- Leading Change. The ability to establish an organizational vision and bring about strategic change to meet organizational goals.
  Competencies: *creativity and innovation, external awareness, flexibility, resilience, strategic thinking, vision.*
- Leading People. The ability to lead people toward meeting the organization's vision, mission, and goals; and, provide an inclusive workplace that fosters the development of others, and facilitates cooperation and teamwork.
  Competencies: *conflict management, leveraging diversity, developing others, team building.*
- Results Driven. The ability to meet organizational goals and customer expectations; and, make decisions that produce high quality results by applying technical knowledge, analyzing problems, and calculating risks.
  Competencies: *accountability, customer service, decisiveness, entrepreneurship, problem solving, technical credibility.*
- Business Acumen. The ability to manage human, financial, and information resources strategically.
  Competencies: *financial-, human capital-, and technology management.*
- Building Coalitions. The ability to build coalitions internally and with other public and private sector organizations to achieve common goals.
  Competencies: *partnering, political savvy, influencing/negotiating.*

Of vital importance are fundamental competencies that serve as a foundation for each of the ECQs. These personal attributes are critical to successful performance as well as success in life, and include the following: interpersonal skills, integrity and honesty, oral communication skills, written communication skills, continual learning, and public service motivation.

Uniformed Service Competencies
The uniformed services must continually develop their officers into exceptional leaders. An important method for accomplishing this is ongoing development of core leader competencies within each of the services. These competencies define leadership requirements and performance expectations. The ***Navy Leadership Competency Model*** (NLCM) is a guide to the essential behaviors and knowledge that are needed to ensure that its leaders are effective and achieve excellent work performance in their positions. The competency model applies to every level and position of leadership. Much like the OPM Core Qualifications, the NLCM is very similar and based on five core competencies. The following abridged excerpts are illustrative.

- Accomplishing Mission. The ability to make timely and effective decisions, and produce results through strategic planning and the implementation and evaluation of programs and policies.
  Competencies: *responsibility, accountability, authority, decisiveness, risk management, problem solving, continuous improvement, technical credibility.*
- Leading People. The ability to design and implement strategies that maximize personnel potential and foster high ethical standards.
  Competencies: *developing people, team building, professionalism.*
- Leading Change. Encompasses the ability to develop and implement an organizational vision that integrates key program goals, priorities and values, and create an environment that encourages creative thinking and innovation.
  Competencies: *creativity and innovation, vision, strategic thinking, external awareness, flexibility, service motivation.*
- Working with People. Involves the ability to explain, advocate, and express facts and ideas in a convincing manner, and negotiate with individuals and groups internally and externally.
  Competencies: *influencing and negotiating, partnering, political awareness, oral communication, written communication.*
- Resource Stewardship. Involves the ability to acquire and administer human, financial, material, and information resources in a manner that instills public trust and accomplishes the mission; and, to use new technology to enhance decision-making.
  Competencies: *financial management, leveraging technology, human resource management.*

To be a truly effective leader, officers need to continually strengthen their core competencies which will, in turn, better align individuals with the PHS mission by improving and empowering their performance excellence.

LEADERSHIP PRINCIPLES

Much is written about principles, competencies and qualities that exemplify an outstanding leader. Leadership is a privilege that must be earned. It requires strength of character and comes with an obligation to lead others with integrity, to show respect for others, to provide a captivating vision, and to achieve successful outcomes. The following leadership principles are derived from recognized leadership values of the uniformed services, business and corporate life, and from literature based upon academic research. The principles are written contextually, such that they have greater relevance to PHS commissioned officers, and begin with the importance of personal integrity.

— PERSONAL VALUES —

▲ *Maintain Absolute Integrity*

Maintain absolute integrity is first among *The Eight Universal Laws of Leadership* of Lt. General (Ret.) William Cohen. Integrity is defined as adherence to moral and ethical standards, and it is yours alone to preserve. Personal integrity is the hallmark of an officer and leader – it is the most important attribute and is essential to the formation of interpersonal trust. What you stand for, and whether you are willing to stand up for what is right, will affect your decisions throughout your career. Your performance of duties and professional relations with others must be consistently ethical, because other officers determine their level of trust in you on the basis of your honesty and character. Senior officers set the tone of an organization, and they must act honorably for the organization to flourish. Transparency of processes and actions, coupled with accountability, are essential features of personal and corporate integrity. Senior officers are cognizant of the importance of acting responsibly and taking the high road when they make official decisions. For example, they must be vigilant to promote fairness and equity toward subordinates, keeping in mind the importance of merit as the basis for advancement. To do otherwise will undermine the leader's authority and weaken esprit de corps within the PHS Corps.

▲ *Know Yourself and Seek Self-Improvement*

"*Knowing yourself is the beginning of all wisdom*" (Aristotle). To know yourself is a critical leadership principle in all uniformed services and major business enterprises. Everyone has an internal narrative of who they are, but that may not be how we appear to others. Real changes are often needed to unify one's stated, idealized values with actual behavior. Officers must have a high degree of self-awareness about their strengths, weaknesses and tendencies – they must know themselves – before they can effectively lead others. The fundamental truth is that, unless a person first learns about him- or herself, it will be difficult to progress. Honestly evaluate your strong and weak personal qualities, moral and ethical stances, likes and dislikes, and life goals. The objective is to know your baseline and, with a specific plan, the areas you want to improve upon. Take initiative to improve yourself through reading, listening, observing, training, and seeking others' opinions. Having a good role model or mentor can be particularly important in this endeavor.

▲ Be Technically Proficient

PHS officers are expected to be highly competent in their chosen profession, knowledgeable about public health principles, and have key leadership competencies. Throughout an officer's career, there are opportunities to broaden knowledge and experience, oftentimes in areas that might not directly relate to one's profession. Obtain feedback about your performance and determine what knowledge and skill sets are needed. Expend the effort to become proficient, by seeking appropriate training from institutional sources, technically competent colleagues, and through field work. Additionally, learn about the Public Health Service in order to attain a solid grounding and true sense of purpose in mission fulfillment.

▲ Seek Responsibility and Take Responsibility

Commitment to accomplishing the PHS mission entails taking responsibility in several ways. All officers should become involved in support activities that strengthen the PHS. The PHS will only be effective if its officers take personal responsibility for the ongoing improvement of programs and systems. Seek a variety of leadership positions that provide an opportunity to accept responsibility in different activities and environments, which will expand and enrich your experience. Officers show commitment by taking ownership of identified problems and seeing them through to complete resolution. Take responsibility for your actions and decisions, and be accountable, even when the outcome is unsuccessful. If a decision turns out to be mistaken, acknowledge the error and immediately remedy the matter. And, officers must assume responsibility for their behavior within and outside the uniformed service. These are important indicators of an increased level of maturity.

— RELATIONAL VALUES —

▲ Articulate the Vision and Mission

The exceptional leader is able to present a compelling vision of the future that is at once challenging, yet achievable. The leader's vision provides a strategic intent to accomplish an end product that is aspirational, which engages and inspires people to enlist in the cause. A leader's words, actions and emotions also send a message, so leaders who are passionate about their vision and their desire to bring it to fruition can reinforce the impact of their message upon listeners. Listeners need to understand the importance of their role in the shared vision and mission, and how their contributory efforts are critical to its accomplishment. In *10 Characteristics of an Effective Vision* by G. Ambler, ten features are believed necessary for an effective vision: future focused, clear and easily understood, sufficiently directional to shape decision-making, relevant to the organization, purpose driven, values based, challenging, unique, vivid and inspiring. Officers should continually seek opportunities to develop their speaking skills, for those who are effective communicators have a distinct advantage in conveying visions in a clear and convincing manner.

▲ Get Out in Front and Set the Example

"Leading by example" – that succinct statement says much about those officers who possess good leadership qualities. Be well groomed and set the standard for proper uniform wear. Show consistent integrity in your actions and decisions, being careful to avoid being swayed by prejudice, interpersonal or organizational politics, or in showing unmerited partiality. Importantly, show initiative, performance excellence, and an optimistic, "can-do" attitude when completing both routine and mission-critical tasks, and become a role model for the team. Instill confidence and develop leadership potential in colleagues and those who are subordinate in rank by providing opportunities to collaborate and share in the decision-making process, and by delegating authority and responsibility for important tasks. Commend those who meet or exceed expectations in carrying out their duties and responsibilities, and publicly recognize individual and team accomplishments.

▲ Know and Respect Others

Sensitivity to the rights, needs and views of others – fellow officers and those with whom you interact – is a leadership trait. With today's global interdependence and workplace diversity, that includes having cultural competence and a desire to develop genuine interest in people of all backgrounds. The leader with emotional intelligence places a high value on understanding behavioral and emotional context and its impact on his/her interactions with others. By showing a concern for others' welfare, leaders help create an emotional bridge between individuals that can lead to better and more productive partnering to achieve common objectives and goals. According to Cuddy, et al., authors of *Connect, Then Lead*, research indicates that the way to lead is to begin with warmth. Even small nonverbal signals – a nod, a smile, an open gesture – show people that you are pleased to be in their company and attentive to their concerns. Prioritizing warmth and combining it with strength helps connect with those around you, demonstrating that you hear them, understand them, and can be trusted by them. Maintain a work environment that is pleasant, energizing and empowering for everyone. PHS officers will find that those who serve the public health mission with excellence and with respect for others derive enjoyment and significant gratification in their work.

▲ Communicate and Inform

Throughout the implementation stages of a vision/mission, it is important that leaders give well thought out directions and expectations to others, while at the same time giving them ownership and responsibility for the completion of meaningful tasks. Be accepting when mistakes are made and view such occurrences as learning opportunities. Keep your team informed about progress being made in completing tasks and achieving project milestones; clarify and amplify operational instructions, as needed; and, alert members to potential problems. Always be open and transparent when describing significant actions taken and planned, program direction, and modifications to an agreed-upon plan. Clarity of purpose with respect to a leader's actions should be of paramount importance. Communication is two-way; therefore, regularly talk with team members, allow for open discussion of issues and alternative approaches, and listen carefully in order to fully understand and appreciate the concerns, thoughts and ideas of others.

▲ Make Sound and Timely Decisions

Officers need to be decisive in carrying out their duties, and accountable for their actions and decisions. Take the initiative to problem-solve issues, and be responsive and timely in your decision-making. Leaders must be able to objectively evaluate issues or situations, understand the impact of options upon the organization, and make sound decisions based upon the estimations. Be open to the advice and suggestions of colleagues, and seek guidance from knowledgeable persons when in doubt about pertinent facts. Transparency of the basis for a particular decision is important to gain understanding and acceptance. Once a decision is made, take responsibility for it. If there are errors of judgment, remedy the situation and move forward with fortitude. Officers who make the effort to maintain a positive attitude in spite of setbacks will receive great personal satisfaction and self-respect.

▲ Develop New Leaders

An important officer leadership principle is the ongoing development of new leaders. Succession planning (succession management) ensures that there are highly qualified people who can seamlessly transition into leadership positions as officers retire, as well as lead the organization into the future. Kevin Groves notes that the process is best accomplished by integrating a program of leadership development with succession planning. Such a program includes an effective mentoring network, full involvement of leaders in identifying high potential individuals, developmental programs, and a supportive organizational culture. Developmental activities include education, leader training, and experiential growth. Leadership growth opportunities may be provided through placement in a variety of settings and increasingly responsible positions; for example, through project-based learning, details, rotational assignments in different programs, and team leader positions.

PHS LEADERSHIP COMPETENCY MODEL

The U.S. Army Leadership Requirements Model (LRM) organizes the disparate requirements and expectations of leaders into a single schematic model. It identifies the two primary sets of requirements as the following:

- *Attributes:* Character – the values and identity of the leader; Presence – the leader's outward appearance, demeanor, actions and words; and, Intellect – the mental and social faculties the leader applies in the act of leading.
- *Competencies:* Leads – leads others, influences, builds trust, sets example, communicates; Develops – creates a positive environment, prepares self, develops others, stewards the profession; and, Achieves – accomplishes tasks, missions and organizational goals.

Using the Army LRM, Navy LCM and Office of Personnel Management ECQ, a USPHS Leadership Competency Model might be depicted as shown below. In this model, personal attributes are the fundamental competencies that, when combined with applied leadership principles, provide the foundation for five core competencies that are essential for PHS officers to attain.

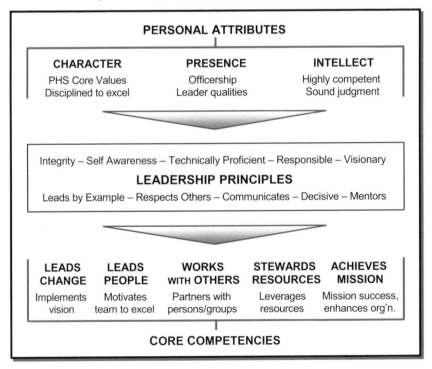

PERSONAL ATTRIBUTES

CHARACTER	PRESENCE	INTELLECT
PHS Core Values	Officership	Highly competent
Disciplined to excel	Leader qualities	Sound judgment

Integrity – Self Awareness – Technically Proficient – Responsible – Visionary

LEADERSHIP PRINCIPLES

Leads by Example – Respects Others – Communicates – Decisive – Mentors

LEADS CHANGE	LEADS PEOPLE	WORKS WITH OTHERS	STEWARDS RESOURCES	ACHIEVES MISSION
Implements vision	Motivates team to excel	Partners with persons/groups	Leverages resources	Mission success, enhances org'n.

CORE COMPETENCIES

Leadership References: *Refer to Selected References, Page 183.*

CHAPTER THREE

UNIFORMED SERVICE
COURTESY & PROTOCOL

Each of the uniformed services has developed courtesies, customs and traditions that complement its legacy of service to the Nation. These protocols and traditions are meant to enhance interpersonal relations, maintain discipline, and provide a heritage for future service personnel. Observance of such protocol is required, and PHS officers should render proper courtesy at all times.

> ADDRESS & GREETING
> COMING TO ATTENTION
> FLAG ETIQUETTE
> HEADGEAR
> POSITION OF HONOR
> PRECEDENCE OF MILITARY SERVICES
> RENDERING HONORS
> SALUTING

Address & Greeting

USE OF TITLES

In the uniformed services, there is a protocol regarding how members are to address one another. A primary purpose of this form of courtesy is that it is an appropriate sign of respect among uniformed personnel.

Personnel who are of subordinate rank address a superior as "Sir" or "Ma'am," by their rank, or by rank and surname. The superior officer addresses a subordinate, whether a commissioned officer or an enlisted service member, by rank, or by rank and surname. In informal work circumstances, officers will usually address each other by their given names. When in formal situations or when outside personnel are present, officers should use prescribed forms of address.

Titles of service rank consist of two groups:

- Titles of rank are the same for personnel in the U.S. Coast Guard, Navy, National Oceanic and Atmospheric Administration (NOAA), and Public Health Service; and
- Titles of rank are the same for commissioned personnel in the U.S. Air Force, Army, and Marine Corps, but differ for enlisted personnel among these services.

Enlisted Personnel. The term *rate* refers to the rank of Navy enlisted personnel. The rate, or grade, always precedes an enlisted person's/sailor's surname. A chief petty officer is addressed as "Chief," "Senior Chief" or "Master Chief." Chief warrant officers may be addressed as "Mister" or "Ms."

The military grade, or rank, in the Air Force, Army and the Marine Corps precedes an enlisted airman's/soldier's/Marine's surname. A warrant officer is addressed as "Mister" or "Ms.," and those above the rank of warrant officer (W-1) in less formal circumstances are addressed as "Chief."

Commissioned Officers. The rank always precedes an officer's surname. In conversation and greetings (cf., written communication), titles of commissioned officers are as follows:

- All lieutenants – first and second lieutenants are addressed *Lieutenant*.
- All colonels – lieutenant colonel and colonel are addressed *Colonel*.
- All commanders – lt. commander and commander are addressed *Commander*.
- All admirals – rear, vice, admiral, and fleet admiral are addressed *Admiral*.
- All generals – brigadier, major, lieutenant, and general are addressed as *General*.

Coast Guard and Navy officers below the rank of commander may be addressed as "Mr. (surname)" or "Ms. (surname)" during routine duty, although this custom is no longer specified by regulation.

Descriptive Titles. In all uniformed service branches, a descriptive title may be used instead of rank for certain officers. For example, officers in the dental and medical professions may be addressed as "Doctor" regardless of rank (except for flag officers, who are always addressed as "Admiral").

Clergy may be addressed as "Chaplain" regardless of rank or religion, although Roman Catholic and Episcopal chaplains may prefer and be properly addressed as "Father" and Jewish chaplains as "Rabbi." During official introductions, these officers' ranks should be used.

By custom, the officer who commands a ship is addressed as "Captain" (or "Skipper") regardless of his rank. Similarly, the executive officer of a ship is addressed as "Commander," and may be referred to as the "Executive Officer" or "XO." The USPHS commanding officer is the Surgeon General who is addressed as "Surgeon General (*surname*)" or "Admiral."

By custom, the head of an Air Force, Army or Marine Corps base or unit is referred to as "the Commanding Officer" or "CO."

The following table shows the equivalent titles of commissioned officer ranks at each pay grade.

UNIFORMED SERVICE TITLES OF RANK

PAY GRADE	NAVY/COAST GUARD NOAA/PHS	ARMY	AIR FORCE MARINE CORPS
01	Ensign ENS	Second Lieutenant 2LT	Second Lieutenant 2nd Lt.
02	Lieutenant Jr Grade LTJG	First Lieutenant 1LT	First Lieutenant 1st Lt.
03	Lieutenant LT	Captain CPT	Captain Capt.
04	Lieutenant Commander, LCDR	Major MAJ	Major Maj.
05	Commander CDR	Lieutenant Colonel LTC	Lieutenant Colonel Lt. Col.
06	Captain CAPT	Colonel COL	Colonel Col.
07	Rear Admiral Lower Half, RDML	Brigadier General BG	Brigadier General Brig. Gen.
08	Rear Admiral Upper Half, RADM *Director, NOAA Corps*	Major General MG	Major General Maj. Gen.
09	Vice Admiral VADM *Surgeon General, PHS*	Lieutenant General LTG	Lieutenant General Lt. Gen.
10	Admiral ADM *Assistant Secretary for Health, PHS Chief of Naval Operations Commandant of the Coast Guard*	General GEN *Army Chief of Staff*	General Gen. *Air Force Chief of Staff Commandant of the Marine Corps*
11	Fleet Admiral FADM [Wartime only]	General of the Army [Wartime only]	General of the Air Force [Wartime only]

Handshake

When shaking hands, the subordinate service member should wait until the senior officer offers his/her hand. When gloves are prescribed, you can remove your right glove, time permitting, when being introduced outdoors; when indoors, remove both gloves. The proper way to shake hands is to keep your hand in a vertical plane, extending your hand with the thumb up and fingers pointed outward. The two hands connect "web to web" in a comfortably firm, solid grip. Shake with two or three smooth hand pumps.

Coming to Attention

The position of attention is a uniformed service courtesy, and is the basic military stance that indicates a person is alert and ready. The position of attention is also the preposition for facing and marching movements.

When to be at Attention
Subordinate personnel in uniform come to attention in prescribed situations. PHS officers should assume the position of attention in certain circumstances:

- When called to attention by the officer in charge.
- When rendering a salute (see the Section *Saluting*).
- When being formally spoken to by a senior officer.
- While the National Anthem is being played indoors (no salute).
- When a senior officer enters a room or joins a table of uniformed personnel, it is proper for those present to stand. When an officer of superior rank enters a room and the command is given, "Attention" or "Attention on Deck," all stand at attention. Alternatively, should a junior officer who first sees a superior officer announce, for example, "Ladies and Gentlemen, the Surgeon General!" all personnel stand at attention. Unless entering for the purpose of addressing the group, the superior officer promptly responds, "As you were." The room is again called to attention when the officer departs. Note that the room is not called to attention when an officer of equal or higher rank is already in the room.

How to Stand at Attention
Stand upright and assume the position of attention by bringing the heels together in line with the feet pointing out equally at a 45-degree angle. Rest the weight of the body evenly on the heels and balls of the feet. Keep the legs straight without stiffening or locking the knees. Hold the body erect with the hips level, stomach in, chest lifted and arched, and the shoulders square. The arms hang straight without stiffness and, with the hands turned inward, curl the fingers loosely so that the tips of the thumbs are alongside and touching the first joint of the forefingers. Keep the thumbs straight along the seams of the trouser legs or mid-point of the thigh for a skirt, with fingers touching the pants/skirt. The head is held erect and square, facing forward and relaxed, with the chin drawn in so that the alignment of the head and neck is vertical. No smiling and remain silent.

Flag Etiquette

PUBLIC HEALTH SERVICE FLAG

The U.S. Public Health Service Indoor Flags are of two types – the *Color*, which includes the PHS Flag, Surgeon General's and Deputy Surgeon General's Flags; and, the *Distinguishing Flag* (DF) for an Assistant Surgeon General. All flag rank officers are authorized to display a DF in conjunction with the U.S., HHS, and/or PHS Flag on ceremonial and other occasions, provided that he/she is the senior flag officer present. PHS Flags displayed out of doors are known as Outdoor Flags and include three types – *Dress, Fair Weather*, and *Storm*. Whenever the U.S. Flag is flown at half mast, so is the PHS Flag. When the U.S. flag is displayed indoors with PHS flags, it is placed in the honor position of the flag's own right (i.e., the observer's left), with all other flags arranged to the left of the U.S. flag in decreasing order of precedence. When displayed in a flag line (e.g., on the stage of an auditorium), the arrangement is as follows: U.S. Flag, Department of Health and Human Services Flag, PHS Flag, and the highest ranking Admiral's Flag. Typically, a total of only four flags will be displayed.

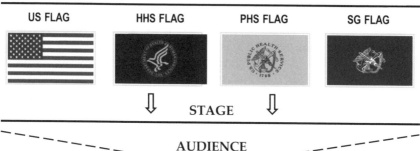

| US FLAG | HHS FLAG | PHS FLAG | SG FLAG |

⇓   STAGE   ⇓

AUDIENCE

UNITED STATES FLAG

The United States Code, Title 4, Chapter 1 and Title 36, Chapter 10 are the primary laws that govern the handling and display of the U.S. Flag. The flag consists of thirteen horizontal stripes, seven red and six white, which alternate with the red stripes on the outside. The canton or union jack contains fifty white stars, with alternating numbers of six and five per row, on a blue field. The proportional size of the flag is 10 : 19 (width : length).

The terms flag, color, standard, or ensign may be used to designate the national flag. The *National Color* is carried by dismounted units, such as a Color Guard, with the flag trimmed with a golden yellow fringe. The *Standard* refers to the national flag when mounted on vehicles. The *National Ensign* is the term used for the national flag when flown from boats and ships.

Raising and Lowering the Flag

Morning colors (Naval, Coast Guard term) or reveille (Army, Air Force term) is the daily ceremony of raising the national flag, and evening colors or retreat is the ceremony of lowering the national flag. The national flag is raised briskly and lowered ceremoniously. Uniformed service personnel face the flag, come to attention and render a salute while the flag is hoisted or lowered, with the salute held until the last note of the bugle call or "To the Colors." In the evening, "Retreat" is played prior to "To the Colors", at which time personnel come to attention and face the flag, and render the salute at the first note of "To the Colors." If driving a vehicle, come to a stop and all occupants sit quietly until the music ends. The U.S. flag is displayed between sunrise and sunset, and during evening hours only if properly illuminated.

Displaying the Flag

There are numerous rules for displaying the U.S. flag and those which follow are most pertinent to uniformed services.

Indoors. When the U.S. flag is displayed indoors with other flags, it is placed in the position of honor, which is to the flag's own right (i.e., the observer's left), with all other flags arranged to the left of the U.S. flag in decreasing order of precedence. No other flag or pennant should be placed to the right or above the U.S. flag. If a podium is present, the U.S. flag is placed to the right of the staging area in advance of the audience, and other flags to the left of the podium (Figure 1). The U.S. flag is centered and its staff is placed vertically at the highest point among a number of flags of states or localities or pennants grouped and displayed from staffs (Figure 2). When the U.S. flag is displayed with another flag where staffs are crossed, the U.S. flag is placed on its own right with its staff positioned in front of the staff of the other flag (Figure 3). If displayed flat against a wall (indoors or outdoors), either horizontally or vertically, the flag's union (stars) is positioned at the top and to the flag's own right (Figure 4).

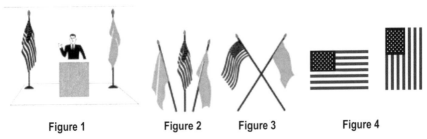

| Figure 1 | Figure 2 | Figure 3 | Figure 4 |

Source: U.S. Navy Website

Outdoors. When displayed outdoors, the U.S. flag is always positioned at the top of the flagpole when other flags are flown on the same pole. When separate flag poles are used for the national flag with other flags, the U.S. flag is placed in the position of honor, to its own right; the other flags may be the same size, but not larger than the U.S. flag, nor may other flags be placed higher than the U.S. flag; and, the U.S. flag is always the first to be raised and the last to be lowered. When flown with flags of other nations, each flag should be approximately the same size and displayed on a separate pole of the same height; all flags are raised and lowered simultaneously. When displayed on a car, the U.S. flag staff is affixed firmly to the chassis or clamped to the front right fender.

Parading the Flag

In procession, the national flag is always accorded the place of honor, which is the marching right or flag's own right (i.e., the viewer's left). When carried with another flag(s), the U.S. flag is positioned to its own right or, if there is a line of other flags, it may be carried in front of the center of that line. When the flag passes in procession, uniformed personnel face the flag and salute at that moment, whereas those in formation salute upon command of the officer in charge. Persons not in uniform place their right hand over the heart; men with a hat remove it with the right hand and hold it at the left shoulder, the hand being over the heart.

The Flag in Mourning

Only the President of the United States or a state governor can order the U.S. flag be lowered to half-staff (*half-mast* in the Navy). When flown at half-staff, the U.S. flag is first hoisted to the peak for an instant and then lowered to a position one-half the distance between the top and bottom of the staff. The flag is again raised to the peak before being lowered for the day. On Memorial Day, the U.S. flag is displayed at half-staff until noon, at which time it is raised to full staff.

The National Anthem and Pledge of Allegiance

When the national anthem is played or sung indoors, uniformed personnel stand at attention facing the flag; when played outdoors, personnel stand at attention and render a salute to the flag at the first note of the anthem, and hold the salute until the last note. When the flag is not displayed or not in view, uniformed personnel face toward the music.

During recitation of the pledge of allegiance indoors, uniformed personnel remain silent and stand at attention facing the flag; when recited outdoors, personnel remain silent, stand at attention and hold a salute to the flag.

Persons not in uniform place their right hand over the heart during the national anthem and pledge of allegiance; men remove their headdress with the right hand and hold it at the left shoulder, the hand being over the heart.

Uniformed service members and veterans who are present, but not in uniform, may render a salute during hoisting, lowering, or passing of the flag, and salute the flag during the National Anthem.

Folding the Flag

There is a traditional method for folding the United States flag (see Figures).

> **Step 1.** Two persons hold the flag parallel to the ground, waist-high. Fold the lower striped half of the flag over the blue field of stars.

> **Step 2.** Fold the flag again lengthwise – begin with the folded edge and bring it up to meet the open edges, with the blue field on the outside.

> **Step 3.** A triangular fold is started by bringing the striped corner of the folded edge to meet the open edge of the flag. Then fold the outer point inward, parallel with the open edge, to form a second triangle. The triangular folding is continued until the entire length of the flag is folded in this manner, and only the blue field and margin are visible.

> **Step 4.** Fold down the square into a triangle and tuck the margin inside the folds. Folding the U.S. flag will take thirteen folds: two lengthwise folds and eleven triangular folds.

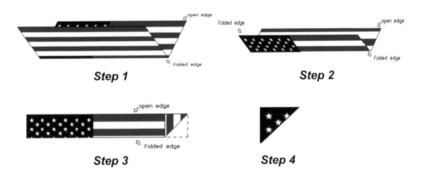

Headgear

Outdoors. When wearing the uniform outdoors, the cap or head cover must always be worn. The cap should never be removed or raised as a form of salutation. The cap need not be worn outside in an area designated by the local commander or uniform authority as a "covered area." For example, a covered area might be the transit area among a group of adjacent buildings. Some areas where the cap would normally not be worn include, for example, an outdoor restaurant. For safety reasons, caps are to be removed and secured upon entering an active aircraft landing zone or airfield tarmac.

Indoors. Uniformed service personnel remove their cap when entering a building, and remain uncovered while indoors. Removing the cap is optional when entering a commercial or public building such as a hotel or an airport.

Position of Honor

The position of honor is always to the right. Thus, junior officers ride, sit, or walk to the left of senior officers. The place of honor in an automobile is the right back seat, although some senior officers prefer to sit in the front passenger seat. When entering the back seat of an automobile from the right side, officers enter in inverse order of rank, allowing the senior officer to enter last and sit on the right side; the senior then is the first to disembark. Alternatively, safety permitting, the junior officer will open and close the right rear door for the senior officer, and the junior officer will enter through the left rear door. If three officers are in the back seat, the junior officer sits in the middle; alternatively, the junior officer should move to the front passenger seat if unoccupied.

When there is a head table at a meeting or official function, the place of honor is to the right of the chairperson or host or the center podium. Senior officers are also accorded the most desirable seats in all settings. A junior officer should open a door to allow the senior officer to enter first, and then pass through after the senior officer.

Precedence of Military Services

For ceremonies and parades in which several military services are participating, service precedence has been established based upon a determination of when each service was formed. That date may actually be, for the Army, Marine Corps, and Navy, when the Continental Congress passed initiating resolutions. In accordance with Department of Defense directive 1005.8, *Order of Precedence of Members of Armed Forces of the United States When in Formations*, service members take precedence in the following order:

Army [June 1775]

Marine Corps [November 1775]

Navy [October 1775, abolished February 1781, Reinstated September 1781]

Air Force [September 1947]

Coast Guard [August 1790]

The Coast Guard, in the Department of Homeland Security, shall take precedence immediately after the Navy, during any period when it operates as part of the Navy.

A member of the senior military service, among those present, will bear the national colors, and the uniformed service flags will be carried in order of seniority from their own right to the left.

There are currently no regulations pertaining to precedence with respect to the Public Health Service Commissioned Corps [1889] and the NOAA Commissioned Corps [1917].

Rendering Honors

Traditional honors may be provided to flag officers and senior government officials during ceremonial occasions, including Surgeon General or Secretarial-level commissioning, change of command and swearing-in ceremonies, and retirement ceremonies of officers at all ranks.

The honors are based upon the Naval custom of "Tending the Side," which is a piping ceremony with sideboys that originated when visitors were hoisted aboard ships using a boatswain's chair. Today, high ranking officers and officials may be honored with the piping ceremony. That courtesy may be combined with the sounding of a ceremonial "ship's" bell.

Honors are rendered at the time officers/officials enter and proceed to the staging area, and at the end of a ceremony during departure of the official party. When an official begins entry to the room, the bell is rung a prescribed number of times, with each gong sounded as a pair of two rings in quick succession. The number of gongs corresponds with the number of sideboys, appropriate to the officer's/official's rank. Immediately following the gongs, the officer/official is announced by rank or position, followed by "arriving" ("departing" at end of the ceremony); such as, "Captain, United States Public Health Service, arriving." The boatswain's (bōs'n's) pipe is sounded as the officer/dignitary begins to pass between two facing ranks, each having an equal number of sideboys, who hold their salutes throughout the passage.

The appropriate number of gongs is as follows:

8 Gongs – Senior HHS official, Admiral or Vice Admiral (o-10, o-9)

6 Gongs – Rear Admiral (o-8, o-7)

4 Gongs – Captain or Commander (o-6, o-5)

2 Gongs – Lieutenant Commander and below (o-4 and below).

Saluting

The military salute has an uncertain origin, but evolved through history. It may be related to knights in armor who raised the face visor on their helmets to identify themselves and as a gesture of friendship. Today, the right hand salute is an honored tradition of greeting and respect among service personnel.

The hand salute is rendered to uniformed service commissioned officers, warrant officers, the President of the United States, senior U.S. government officials, Medal of Honor recipients, and officers of friendly foreign countries. Salutes are returned, as prescribed, to all members of the uniformed services. Due to its importance within military protocol, it is essential that all PHS officers properly render hand salutes, with precision.

Forms of Salute

An officer normally uses the hand salute. However, if under arms (e.g., carrying a rifle), render the salute prescribed for the weapon with which armed. The sword or saber salute involves bringing the hilt to the chin, the flat of the blade opposite to the right eye, sword point up, and a subsequent lowering of the point to the ground, until the person to whom the salute is rendered has passed six paces. Cannon salutes are reserved to honor high civilian and military officials. The number of cannon blasts is prescribed according to the honored person's rank.

Hand Salute Basics

Both an initial hand salute and a return hand salute are required. The salute is always initiated by a person of junior rank, whether enlisted or officer, to an officer who is senior in rank. The initiating salute is held until after a return salute or acknowledgement is made by the higher ranking officer. When rendering a salute, one's head and eyes are turned to the person being saluted or to the Colors.

If *standing,* the junior officer salutes from the position of attention. When *walking,* the salute should be initiated in sufficient time to allow a response by the senior officer; a general guide is to initiate the salute between six and ten paces. It is courteous to accompany one's salute with a verbal greeting to the senior officer such as "Good morning (afternoon, evening), Sir/Ma'am." Upon saluting, the senior officer should similarly reply with the subordinate's rank ("Good morning, Lieutenant"). If two officers or an officer and enlisted member approach one another with the intent of formally conversing, salutes are exchanged upon meeting and again after the conversation, before departing. When approaching a group of officers with various ranks, the initiating salute is directed toward the senior officer.

How to Salute

The hand salute is performed by raising the right hand smartly, fingers extended and joined, palm down and slightly turned toward the face. The hand is brought upward until the tip of the forefinger/middle finger touches the right front corner of the headdress. If wearing a non-billed cap, touch the forehead slightly to the right and above the right eye or the right front corner of eyeglasses. Hold the upper arm horizontal with the elbow slightly forward,

U.S. Naval Institute, with permission.

the forearm inclined at a 45 degree angle, and the hand and wrist straight. To complete the salute, the hand is dropped smartly to the position of attention at one's side.

When to Salute
Personnel in uniform and with head cover are required to render salutes in the following instances.

- When approaching a senior officer in uniform.
- When saluted by junior officers or enlisted personnel.
- When passing a senior officer walking in the same direction, the subordinate holds a salute when abreast stating, "By your leave, Sir/Ma'am;" the senior officer returns the salute with "Carry on" or "Very well."
- Upon the command, "Present, arms."
- To the national color (U.S. flag mounted on a flagstaff with finial) outdoors, holding the salute six steps distance before until six steps after it passes by, or before and after passing it.
- At morning and evening colors (reveille and retreat), when the national flag is being raised or lowered. Personnel face the flag or, if not visible, face in the direction of the flag and/or music and hold the salute from the first note of "Reveille." Note that in the evening, the bugle call "Retreat" is first sounded and all personnel come to attention; following that, the national anthem or "To the Colors" is played during which all personnel render and hold a salute until the music has finished.
- During the playing of the U.S. National Anthem, the bugle call "To the Colors," "Hail to the Chief," or a foreign national anthem.
- When the Pledge of Allegiance is recited at civilian events outdoors.
- When an official vehicle displaying the rank of a flag/general officer or high level dignitary passes on base.
- When turning over control of formations.
- On ceremonial occasions (e.g., command change, military parades).
- During an indoor promotion or award/recognition ceremony when the proceedings call for the exchange of salutes.

When Saluting is Not Required
- When officers of equal rank approach each other (optional salute).
- When impractical, such as carrying packages in both hands.
- When either the subordinate or senior member is wearing civilian clothes (optional salute).
- When at large public gatherings such as sporting events.
- Indoors and in a "covered" area (except as noted under When to Salute).
- When the national anthem is played or the Pledge of Allegiance is recited indoors (uniformed personnel stand at attention and face the flag).

In each of these instances (not including the national anthem/Pledge of Allegiance), a verbal greeting is appropriate.

Other Situations

Formation. When an individual is in charge of a formation or work detail, he salutes for the group. Formation members do not salute except at the command of the ranking officer. If not already at attention, the commands are: "Attention;" personnel salute at "Present, arms" or "Hand, salute," and complete the salute after the command "Order, arms" or "Ready, two."

Military Installations. When entering a military installation by vehicle, an officer may receive a hand or rifle (if under arms) salute by the gate guard. It is proper for an officer in uniform to return the salute, if it can be done safely; an officer not in uniform may also return the salute as a matter of courtesy, if safe; in either instance, a salute is not required. When driving on a military base, it is customary that vehicles stop while colors are sounded; on Navy and Coast Guard bases, all occupants remain silent in the vehicle, whereas on Army and Air Force bases, the senior person (or all occupants) disembarks and renders the hand salute.

Reporting (pertains to the Armed Forces). If formally reporting to a commanding officer in his/her office, a certain procedure is followed. Upon reaching the office, an officer removes his cover, knocks, and enters the room when called. The service member approaches the officer's desk and stops about two paces away. Come to attention and render a hand salute stating, "Sir/Ma'am, (your *rank, first and last name*) reporting." For example, "Ma'am, Lieutenant Robert Smith reporting."

Ship Boarding. When boarding a uniformed service commissioned vessel, personnel stop at the top of the gangway, turn toward the ship's stern and salute the national ensign. Then, turn to face and salute the officer of the deck (OOD, who may be a commissioned, warrant or senior petty officer). While saluting, state the request "Sir/Ma'am, permission to come aboard," setting foot on deck only after the salute is returned and permission granted. If appropriate, you will say "(your *rank and name*) reporting for duty, Sir/Ma'am." When leaving the ship, face and salute the OOD and request permission to go ashore. When the OOD returns the salute and/or grants permission, walk a few steps, turn and salute the aft ensign, and then disembark.

Veterans and Active Duty Not in Uniform. In accordance with provisions of the 2008 and 2009 Defense Authorization Act, uniformed service personnel and veterans who are present, but not in uniform, may render a hand salute during hoisting, lowering, or passing of the flag, and salute the flag during the National Anthem.

CHAPTER FOUR

OFFICIAL CEREMONY PROTOCOL

Commissioned officers will, at various times throughout their career, attend, plan and participate in official PHS ceremonies, which are an integral part of uniformed service tradition. These formal events are important in recognizing the accomplishments and outstanding service of fellow officers and in building a sense of shared purpose in striving for excellence in one's chosen profession. Ceremonial protocol extends to the final chapter of an officer's life, when military funeral honors are rendered as a sign of respect for those who have so ably served their Nation. [See Appendix A, Ceremony Planning Form.]

AWARDS CEREMONY
CHANGE OF COMMAND CEREMONY
PROMOTION CEREMONY
RETIREMENT CEREMONY
MILITARY FUNERAL HONORS

Awards Ceremony

Awards/decoration ceremonies are held when a number of officers are to be recipients. The presentation of awards in a formal ceremony enhances the significance of the achievements being recognized and serves to bolster esprit de corps. The presenting officer should be superior in rank or position to the highest ranking officer being decorated. A master/mistress of ceremonies, also referred to as the adjutant, will direct the program.

Organizational Sponsor
The USPHS and Federal agencies sponsor semi-annual or annual awards ceremonies in the Washington, DC metropolitan area. Agency ceremonies may recognize both Civil Service and commissioned officer employees. Those officers being recognized whose duty station is outside of OpDiv Headquarters (typically located in the Washington, DC metropolitan area), are generally honored at ceremonies hosted by regional units of their organization.

Event Formality

The formality of the awards ceremony will vary consistent with the organizational level of the host unit, the rank of presiding officials and dignitaries, the location, number of officers being recognized, and the available resources. Within the Washington, DC area, when the Surgeon General or other high-ranking officer is officiating, the awards ceremony is relatively formal and includes the USPHS Honor Cadre and Music Ensemble.

General Format

Arrival. The adjutant begins by requesting guests to "please rise for the arrival of the official party" and calling the room to attention, at which time senior officials enter and proceed to the staging area.

Opening and Remarks. The event opens with presentation of the colors, the National Anthem, and PHS March (optional Invocation). The adjutant then invites the audience to be seated. He/she welcomes the attendees and introduces officers/officials on the stage. Opening remarks are made by the senior officer and/or agency officials. The awards ceremony is attended by supervisory personnel, colleagues and family of the awardees, and remarks should include an expression of appreciation to these individuals for their support of the officers being recognized.

Award Presentations. Awards are presented in order of precedence of the award, from highest to lowest, and then based upon on rank of the recipient, from most senior to junior. The adjutant announces "Attention to orders," in response to which all officers stand at attention and others in the audience rise. The award citation is read for the first awards. The audience is invited to be seated. The adjutant calls one officer at a time, or a group of officers receiving a particular award, to the stage. The officer being recognized takes a position of attention to the left of the senior officer. A group of officers form a line to the left of the senior officer, facing the audience. The adjutant or senior officer may make remarks about the officer/group being recognized. An aide hands the award to the senior officer, who attaches the award to the officer's uniform. If a large group, the senior officer attaches the award to one officer's uniform and an aide hands each of the other officers the written citation with award. The senior officer shakes the hand of the recognized officer(s), and photographs are taken. The officer then salutes the senior officer. The adjutant initiates applause, and the award recipient exits the staging area. The presentation cycle is repeated for each type of award.

Closing. The senior officer/official makes closing remarks. At the conclusion of those remarks, the adjutant asks the audience to rise while the official party departs. Once the official party has left, the adjutant announces "This concludes the awards ceremony. Please join the award recipients for a reception in the (*location*)."

A sample ceremony program outline and staging area schematic follow.

Planning

Planning and preparations for a formal awards ceremony should begin about three months in advance of the event date. Less formal occasions may be planned with less advance time, in accordance with the ceremony particulars. For those officers tasked with planning an awards ceremony, a planning checklist is provided in Appendix A.

Sample Program

OSG AWARDS CEREMONY
— *Program* —

Master of Ceremonies

Arrival of the Official Party

Presentation of the Colors
Surgeon General's Honor Cadre

National Anthem, PHS March
USPHS Music Ensemble

Invocation

Welcome
Director, CC Personnel

Opening Remarks
Presiding Officer

Awards Presentation

Closing Remarks

Departure of the Official Party

Reception

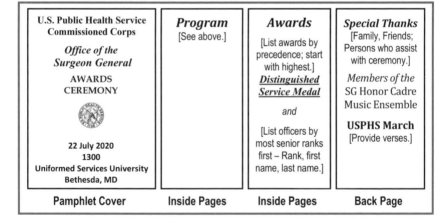

U.S. Public Health Service Commissioned Corps *Office of the Surgeon General* AWARDS CEREMONY [seal] 22 July 2020 1300 Uniformed Services University Bethesda, MD	*Program* [See above.]	*Awards* [List awards by precedence; start with highest.] *Distinguished Service Medal* *and* [List officers by most senior ranks first – Rank, first name, last name.]	*Special Thanks* [Family, Friends; Persons who assist with ceremony.] *Members of the* SG Honor Cadre Music Ensemble **USPHS March** [Provide verses.]
Pamphlet Cover	**Inside Pages**	**Inside Pages**	**Back Page**

Sample Staging Area

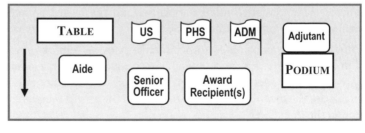

Change of Command Ceremony

The Change of Command ceremony represents a long-standing tradition among the military services for the transfer of leadership. The ceremony is symbolic of the authority that is given to a new officer to properly administer and direct an organizational unit. Because of the importance of the event in the PHS, a number of senior officers and officials may be present. A master/-mistress of ceremonies, also known as the adjutant, will direct the program.

Sponsor and Applicability
In the Public Health Service, Change of Command ceremonies are sponsored by the Office of the Surgeon General (OSG) and/or the Department of Health and Human Services (HHS). These ceremonies are held for the Surgeon General, Acting Surgeon General, and for the appointment of a new chief professional officer (CPO). A Swearing-In ceremony is held for the Assistant Secretary of Health, HHS.

For the appointment of a new Surgeon General, or an Assistant Secretary for Health who will be performing duties as a commissioned officer, when such individuals are not already a career PHS Commissioned Corps officer, the event may include a Commissioning ceremony prior to the Change of Command or Swearing-In component of the program.

Event Formality
The Change of Command ceremony is a formal occasion that requires extensive planning and preparation to ensure a successful event. When carried out to recognize senior HHS or OSG leadership, commissioned officers in attendance should wear the Service Dress or Full Dress uniform, as prescribed. Within the Washington, DC metropolitan area, the ceremony will include the USPHS Honor Cadre and Music Ensemble.

Ceremony Tradition
In the Army, Air Force and Marine Corps, the change of command is performed by the "passing of colors." The outgoing Commander relinquishes authority by passing the guidon (flag of the unit and its commanding officer) to the ranking presiding officer, who in turn passes the flag to the incoming Commander, thereby entrusting to the new Commander responsibility for the unit. In the Navy and Coast Guard, the tradition of relief and assumption of command is carried out through the exchange of the following words: "I relieve you, sir/ma'am", and, "I stand relieved." In the PHS, the change of command tradition for the Surgeon General was formed in 2006, when the outgoing Surgeon General passed a large brass PHS Crest/Seal, mounted on a wood plaque, to the incoming Acting Surgeon General, using words of the Navy ceremony. For chief professional officers, various ceremonial articles may be utilized to complement dialogue (e.g., passing the Nursing Lamp).

General Format

Arrival. The adjutant begins by requesting guests to "please rise for the arrival of the official party" and calling the room to attention. At that time, senior officers/officials enter and proceed to the staging area.

Honors are rendered for Surgeon General and Secretarial-level installations. As each senior officer/official enters the room, a ceremonial bell is rung and they are announced (see *Rendering Honors* in Chapter Three). The Boatswain's pipe is sounded as each HHS dignitary/senior officer passes between the two facing ranks of sideboys, who hold their salutes for the duration of the passage.

Opening and Remarks. The event opens with presentation of the colors, the National Anthem, PHS March, and Invocation. The adjutant then invites the audience to be seated. He/she welcomes the attendees and introduces officers/officials on the stage. Opening remarks are made by senior officers, agency officials and/or guest speakers.

Proceedings. Following the welcome and opening remarks, the Keynote Speaker in ceremonies for the Surgeon General or Assistant Secretary for Health will likely be the Secretary of HHS. If speaking, the Secretary is introduced by the incumbent Assistant Secretary for Health or Surgeon General, and the Assistant Secretary is introduced by the Surgeon General.

If there is a Commissioning and/or Swearing-In component, the Commission is read, the Oath of Office is administered, and frocking (if applicable) occurs at this point in the program.

The outgoing SG or CPO provides farewell remarks. The officer then salutes the presiding official and states, "I stand ready to be relieved." The adjutant announces "Attention to orders," in response to which all officers stand at attention and others in the audience rise. The orders are read and the symbolic passing of the PHS Crest, or CPO Badge and perhaps other article for CPOs, takes place with the expression of the traditional words of relief and assumption of command. The colors of the newly installed incumbent are posted, and the audience is invited to be seated.

Closing and Reception. The new Assistant Secretary, Surgeon General or chief professional officer presents remarks. At the conclusion, the adjutant asks the audience to rise while the official party departs. Once again, the official party is piped while departing between facing ranks of sideboys. When they have left, the adjutant announces "This concludes the ceremony. Please join the Secretary/Surgeon General for a reception in the (*location*)."

A receiving line is formed at the reception which is normally comprised of an aide, the outgoing officer as host and his/her spouse, and the incoming officer and spouse, plus another officer as determined by the host to end the line. If a principal guest and spouse join the line, they stand following the spouse of the host and before the incoming officer.

Planning

Planning and preparations for the Change of Command Ceremony is a high priority event that should begin about four months in advance of the event. For those officers tasked with planning an awards ceremony, a planning checklist is provided in Appendix A. Two sample ceremony program outlines follow, one for the Surgeon General and the other for a CPO.

SG COMMISSIONING & CHANGE OF COMMAND CEREMONY	CHIEF PROFESSIONAL OFFICER CHANGE OF COMMAND CEREMONY
— *Program* —	— *Program* —
Arrival of the Official Party	Master of Ceremonies
Presentation of the Colors	Arrival of the Official Party
National Anthem, PHS March	Presentation of the Colors
Invocation	National Anthem, PHS March
Welcome	Invocation
Keynote Address Secretary, HHS	Welcome
Remarks Guests	Remarks Guests
Musical Interlude	Musical Interlude
Reading of the Commission	Remarks Outgoing CPO
Oath of Office	Attention to Orders
Frocking	Presentation of CPO Badge
Change of Command	Change of Command
Posting of the Colors	Remarks Chief Professional Officer
Address Surgeon General	Departure of the Official Party
Departure of the Official Party	Reception
Reception	

U.S. Public Health Service Commissioned Corps CHIEF PROFESSIONAL OFFICER CHANGE OF COMMAND CEREMONY 22 July 2020 1300 Parklawn Building Rockville, MD	*Program* [See above.]	Pictures and Biographies of New and Outgoing CPOs. Listing of the Category's CPOs by Term of Office.	*Special Thanks* [Family, Friends; Persons who assist with ceremony.] *Members of the* SG Honor Cadre Music Ensemble **USPHS March** [Provide verses.]
Pamphlet Cover	**Inside Pages**	**Inside Pages**	**Back Page**

Promotion Ceremony

Uniformed services traditionally hold promotion ceremonies to formally acknowledge and publicly recognize an officer's appointment to a higher rank. The achievement of a promotion is a significant event in the life of an officer, and the presence of fellow officers serves to reinforce esprit de corps. The presenting officer should be superior in rank or position to the highest ranking officer being promoted. A master/mistress of ceremonies, also referred to as adjutant, will direct the program. Family and friends are invited to share in the officer's accomplishment and participate in the ceremony.

Organizational Sponsor
U.S. Public Health Service officers work in several principal that are hierarchically segmented into operating divisions (OpDivs), agencies, areas/-bureaus/centers/institutes, service units or offices. Depending on the number of officers being promoted, the promotion ceremony is hosted by the highest organizational level starting at the operating division or agency level. Those officers being promoted whose duty station is outside of OpDiv Headquarters (typically located in the Washington, DC metropolitan area) may be honored at ceremonies hosted by local or regional organizational units to allow greater participation and attendance by colleagues, family and friends.

Event Formality
The formality of the promotion ceremony will vary consistent with the organizational level of the host unit, the rank of presiding officials and dignitaries, the location, number of officers being promoted, and the available resources. Within the Washington, DC area, when the Surgeon General or other high-ranking officer is officiating, the promotion ceremony is relatively formal and includes the USPHS Honor Cadre and Music Ensemble.

Event Invitations
An invitation is sent to officers being promoted, which includes a request to invite their supervisor and also designate a family member or close friend to participate in the ceremony of replacing old shoulder boards. The highest ranking official and PHS commissioned officer of the host organization are also invited, with the most senior officer officiating if an Admiral. Other high level managers within the organization should be invited by the host officials.

Event Scheduling
Whereas officers are promoted on the first day of the quarter in which they are eligible, the majority receive their promotions effective 1 July. For that reason, most organizational units schedule one promotion ceremony around that date to cover the ensuing 12-month period, and invite all officers who are to be promoted during that period to be recognized at the ceremony.

General Format

Arrival. The adjutant begins by requesting guests to "please rise for the arrival of the official party" and calling the room to attention, at which time senior officials enter and proceed to the staging area.

Opening and Remarks. The event opens with presentation of the colors, the National Anthem, and PHS March (optional Invocation). The adjutant then invites the audience to be seated. He/she welcomes the attendees and introduces officers/officials on the stage. Opening remarks are made by the senior officer and/or agency officials. The ceremony is attended by supervisory personnel, colleagues and family of the officers being promoted, and remarks should include an expression of appreciation to these individuals for their support of the officers being recognized.

Promotions. Promotion order is by rank, from highest to lowest. Prior to the announcement of each promotion rank, the applicable group files out of the room through a rear exit and proceeds to a holding area near the stage, in alphabetical order. For each promotion rank, the adjutant announces "Attention to Orders," in response to which all officers stand at attention and others in the audience rise. The promotion order is read and the audience is invited to be seated. The adjutant calls one officer at a time to the stage to be promoted, and the officer and family member (or designee if no family member is present) proceed to the stage. The officer being promoted takes a position of attention to the left of the senior officer, and the family member stands to the left of the officer. The adjutant or senior officer may make remarks about the officer, and then introduces the family member or other designee who will assist in the promotion. An aide hands the correct shoulder boards to the senior officer and family member, who replace the old with the new shoulder boards. The senior officer shakes the hand of the recognized officer, photographs are taken, and the promoted officer salutes the senior officer. The adjutant initiates applause, and the promoted officer and family member exit the stage. The program cycle is repeated for each promotion rank.

Closing. The senior officer makes closing remarks. At the conclusion of those remarks, the adjutant asks the audience to rise while the official party departs. Once the official party has left, the adjutant announces "This concludes the ceremony. Please join us for a reception in the (*location*)."

Planning

Planning and preparations for a formal promotion ceremony should begin about four months in advance of the event date. Less formal occasions may be planned with much less advance time, in accordance with the ceremony particulars. For those officers tasked with planning a promotion ceremony, a planning checklist is provided in Appendix A.

A sample ceremony program outline and staging area schematic follow.

*Sample
Program*

NIH PROMOTION CEREMONY
— *Program* —

Master of Ceremonies

Arrival of the Official Party

Presentation of the Colors
Surgeon General's Honor Cadre

National Anthem, PHS March
USPHS Music Ensemble

Invocation

Welcome
Director, NIH

Opening Remarks
Presiding Officer

Promotion Presentation

Closing Remarks

Departure of the Official Party

Reception

Pamphlet Cover	Inside Pages	Inside Pages	Back Page
The Twentieth Annual National Institutes of Health PROMOTION CEREMONY For U.S. Public Health Service Commissioned Officers 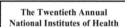 22 July 2020 1300 Natcher Auditorium Bethesda, MD	*Program* [See above.]	*Promotions* *To Captain:* [List officers by last name, first name, category, Agency.] *To Commander:* *Etc.* *Alternatively, list officers by units within the Agency, then by Rank, etc.*	*Special Thanks* [NIH Institutes.] [Family, Friends; Persons who assist with ceremony.] *Members of the* SG Honor Cadre Music Ensemble **USPHS March** [Provide verses.]

*Sample
Staging
Area*

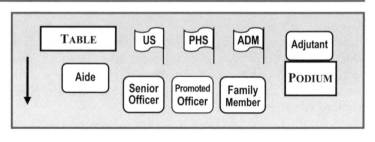

Retirement Ceremony

It is traditional within uniformed services to hold retirement ceremonies to formally acknowledge and publicly recognize an officer's honorable service. This is a significant occasion for all officers – the retiree and the active duty officers in attendance – and it warrants the attention of senior officials to ensure a proper send-off. The retiring officer should be leaving the service with an expression of appreciation for his/her valued work over the years, and with the knowledge that he will continue to be looked upon as a member of the Public Health Service family in retirement. A master/mistress of ceremonies, also referred to as the adjutant, will direct the program. This person may be an officer who is a colleague of the retiree.

Event Formality

The formality of the retirement ceremony will vary consistent with the rank of the retiring officer, and the rank of presiding officials and dignitaries. If the Surgeon General or high-ranking officer is officiating, the ceremony is relatively formal and may include the PHS Honor Cadre and Music Ensemble.

It is appropriate to present the officer with an award (e.g., the PHS Citation) for his career contributions, and is a nice gesture to give a presentation case holding the national flag and devices (e.g., medals and ribbons) earned by the officer while on active duty. In the PHS, the retirement ceremony is a farewell event at which fellow officers, colleagues, family and friends are present, and gifts may be presented to the retiree (cf., a formal military ceremony, where gifts may be withheld during the ceremony).

Event Preparations

The selection of an event location and other particulars, such as the guest speakers and invited guests, should be discussed with the retiring officer. If high-ranking officials are among the official party, planners should contact those persons regarding their availability before deciding on a ceremony date.

Typically, a general invitation is sent by a broadcast e-mail to fellow officers and colleagues within the officer's duty station, and to others specified by the retiring officer. Supervisors and senior officials in the retiree's duty station should be invited individually, and the retiring officer's family should invite close friends by personal communication.

Certain items need to be planned well in advance of the ceremony. For example, a determination of the ceremony location, date, and official party, to include the presiding officer and guest speakers, needs to be set. If an award is planned, there is an extended lead time necessary for approval and transmittal. If a national flag that is flown over a specified site (e.g., U.S. Capitol Building) and/or a letter of recognition from an elected official are desired, those items need attention early in the ceremony preparations.

General Format

The program formality and content can vary considerably. When accompanied by a meal, the ceremony should commence after the meal is finished.

Arrival. For a formal event, family members are escorted as a group to their seats, usually in the first row of the audience. The master of ceremonies then begins by requesting guests to "please rise for the arrival of the official party" and calling the room to attention, at which time the presiding (senior) officer, retiree and other ceremony participants proceed to the staging area, facing the audience (spouse may elect to sit with the retiree).

Opening. The event opens with presentation of the colors, the National Anthem, and PHS March, and Invocation. The master of ceremonies then invites the audience to be seated. He/she welcomes the attendees and introduces officers/officials on the stage.

Remarks. Opening remarks are often made by guest speakers, followed by the presiding officer and/or agency officials. The remarks should include an expression of appreciation to the retiree's family and colleagues for their support of the officer being recognized. The presiding officer or principal speaker should provide a memorable summarization of the retiring officer's career and substantive contributions to the PHS.

Presentations/Recognitions. When there is presentation of a decoration, the master of ceremonies so announces and the retiring officer takes a position of attention to the left of the presiding officer; that officer will read the citation, attach the decoration to the retiring officer's uniform and present the written citation. The presiding officer shakes the hand of the retiring officer, who then salutes the presiding officer (if superior in rank to the retiring officer). Gifts, to include the presentation case, are presented to the retiree at this time, and personal tributes to the retiree may also be made. The retiree's family is invited to come forward for recognition – for example, a *Certificate of Appreciation* or flowers may be presented to the retiree's spouse.

Old Glory Ceremony. At a retiree's request, the Old Gory Ceremony may be performed here, or after reading of the retirement order. (See below, the *Old Glory Flag Passing Ceremony.*)

Remarks of Retiree. The retiring officer is afforded the opportunity to make farewell remarks to those gathered in his honor.

Retirement Orders. The master of ceremonies will announce "Attention to Orders," and all officers stand at attention and others in the audience rise for the reading of the retirement order. The retiring officer rises and takes a position to the left of the presiding officer. After the order is read, the presiding officer presents the *Retirement Certificate* to the retiree. The presiding officer shakes the hand of the retired officer, and photographs are taken.

Closing and Ringing Out Ceremony.   As the ceremony concludes, the retired officer, facing the presiding officer, requests departure:

"Sir, as I have been properly relieved, request permission to leave the deck and to retire." Presiding officer responds: "Permission granted."

The master of ceremonies asks the audience to rise while the official party, led by the retiree and spouse, depart. Because the USPHS traces its origins to ministering to merchant seamen, the retired officer may be "piped over the side" with the Navy custom of sounding bells/gongs to announce a senior officer's arrival or departure from a ship. In the PHS retirement ceremony, this symbolizes the retired officer leaving a ship and going ashore for the last time (see *Rendering Honors* in Chapter Three).

The master of ceremonies announces:

"As (*retiree's rank and name, e.g., CAPT Franklin*) completes his career with the Public Health Service and retires as a commissioned officer with 30 years of active service to his Country, we ring four bells to signify his departure."

The master of ceremonies announces: "Sound (*number – 2, 4, 6, or 8*) bells, (*rank and retiree's name*), departing."

Program planners may want to include two facing ranks of the appropriate number of the retired officer's colleagues to serve as sideboys, through which the retired officer and spouse walk and exit the room.

Reception.   Once the official party has left, the master of ceremonies announces "Ladies and gentlemen, this concludes the ceremony. Please join (*name of retiree*) for a reception and ceremonial cutting of the cake in the (*location*)." The retired officer will cut the first piece of cake with a PHS sword, and then stands with his/her spouse in an area away from the cake to receive and greet guests.

Planning

Planning and preparations for a formal retirement ceremony should begin about four months in advance of the event date, keeping in mind the items discussed above that may need additional lead time. Less formal occasions may be planned with much less advance time, in accordance with ceremony particulars. For those officers tasked with planning a retirement ceremony, a planning checklist is provided in Appendix A.

A sample ceremony program outline and staging area schematic follow.

Sample Program

> ### RETIREMENT CEREMONY
> ### — *Program* —
>
> **Master of Ceremonies**
>
> **Arrival of the Official Party**
>
> **Presentation of the Colors**
> Surgeon General's Honor Cadre
>
> **National Anthem, PHS March**
> USPHS Music Ensemble
>
> **Invocation**
>
> **Guest Speakers**
>
> **Remarks**
> Presiding Officer
>
> **Presentations**
>
> **Old Glory Ceremony**
>
> **Remarks**
> Retiring Officer
>
> **Retirement Order**
>
> **Departure of the Official Party**
>
> **Reception**

U.S. Public Health Service *Retirement Ceremony for* RADM BENJAMIN FRANKLIN 22 July 2020 1300 Uniformed Services University of the Health Sciences Bethesda, MD	*Program* [See above.]	*Biosketch* [Biosketch of retiring officer, to include positions held, accomplishments, academic background, recognitions.]	*Special Thanks* [Family, Friends; Persons who assist with ceremony.] *Members of the* SG Honor Cadre Music Ensemble **USPHS March** [Provide verses.]
Pamphlet Cover	**Inside Pages**	**Inside Pages**	**Back Page**

Sample Staging Area

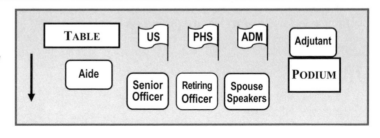

Old Glory Flag Passing Ceremony

Retiring PHS officers may request performance of the flag presentation ceremony known as the Old Glory Ceremony. Although not an official ceremony, it has become customary to include it in the retirement program, upon request, to heighten ceremonial dignity with respect to presentation of the U.S. flag to the retiree. The following version of the ceremony is significantly modified both from the original poem and from military scripts. It includes references to U.S. Public Health Service events in place of military events, and is based upon renditions used in prior PHS retirement ceremonies.

The ceremony text is divided into the number of segments needed to represent each of the ranks held by the retiring officer during his/her career. The following script is based upon a retiring officer with the rank of Captain, so participants will include a master of ceremonies/reader, Lieutenant, Lt. Commander, Commander, and Captain (the retiree). The dramatic nature of this ceremony is enhanced by slow, deliberate movements, so the MC who reads the script and participants who perform facing maneuvers, flag passing, and salutes should not rush. Note that ceremony participants wear gloves. The LT, LCDR, CDR, and CAPT may enter and proceed together to their respective stage positions, or, each officer can enter as their assigned segment is read, face forward and stand at attention. The LT holds the folded flag, with right hand on top.

OLD GLORY CEREMONY SCRIPT

MC: Title 42 of the U.S. Code, the PHS Act, specifically provides that officers retiring from the PHS Commissioned Corps shall be presented with a United States flag as an expression of the Nation's appreciation for their service. The presentation is often marked by the Old Glory Ceremony. A folded American flag is ceremoniously presented to the retiring officer as a symbol of gratitude for his or her dedicated and selfless service to the Department, to the Commissioned Corps, and to the Nation. *[Pause]*

LT enters from Stage Right holding the folded flag – right hand on top – and moves to his/her position on stage, turns to face forward, and stands at attention.

MC: I am the Flag of the United States of America. My name is OLD GLORY. *[Pause]*

I fly atop America's tallest buildings. *[Pause]*

I wave proudly beside our Nation's monuments. *[Pause]*

LCDR enters from Stage Right and moves to position on stage, turns to face forward, and stands at attention.

MC: I stand watch in America over families at home, children at school, and over the sick and weary. *[Pause]*

I lead the procession of flags representing the Department and the Commissioned Corps. Look up and see me! *[Pause]*

CDR enters from Stage Right and moves to position on stage, turns to face forward, and stands at attention.

MC: I stand for freedom. *[Pause]*

I am confident. I am proud. I bow to no one. *[Pause]*

When flown alongside my fellow banners, my head is held a little higher...my colors shine a little truer. *[Pause]*

LT will do a Left Face maneuver and LCDR a Right Face maneuver to face each other. LCDR slowly renders and drops salute, and receives the flag ...right hand on top. LT slowly renders and drops salute. LT will face forward and stand at attention. LCDR will complete an About Face and CDR will complete a Right Face maneuver to face each other.......maneuvers continue during reading.

MC: In times of stress and duress, I am a symbol of hope. *[Pause]*

I am saluted – I am respected. I am recognized all over the world. *[Pause]*

I am revered – I am loved – I am determined and fearless. *[Pause]*

CDR slowly renders and drops salute, and receives the flag...right hand on top. LCDR slowly renders and drops salute. LCDR will face forward and stand at attention. CDR will complete an About Face and take one step forward. CAPT/retiree will take one step forward and make a Right Face maneuver to face CDR.......maneuvers continue during reading.

MC: I have been present during every battle of every war for more than two centuries. Those who serve beneath my stars and stripes fight disease and injury – they protect public health. They conquered yellow fever, rubella, and smallpox – they are leaders in disease prevention. *[Pause]*

Retiree slowly renders and drops salute, and receives the flag...right hand on top. CDR slowly renders and drops salute. CDR will complete an About Face, take one step, and return to original position, face forward and stand at attention. Retiree will take one step back and face forward.

MC: I lead health professionals of many disciplines. I comfort and encourage them when they are overwhelmed. I proudly lead them forward to triumph. *[Pause]*

LT will take one step forward, complete a Left Face and exit the stage.

MC: I served with our Commissioned Corps officers through 9-11, through Hurricanes Katrina, Rita, and Wilma. I served in the Gulf Region, in Iraq and Afghanistan, in Indonesia and the Pacific Basin, in Central and South America – all over the world. *[Pause]*

My health care leaders love me – they cheer me, and I am proud. *[Pause]*

LCDR will take one step forward, complete a Left Face and exit the stage.

MC: I have been soiled, burned, torn and trampled in the streets of those cities and countries that I have helped. It does not hurt me, for I am invincible. I protect, promote, and advance the health and safety of our great Nation. I stand up for the underserved. I have witnessed the heroic efforts of my warriors in the field and trenches of the silent war against disease. *[Pause]*

CDR will take one step forward, complete a Left Face and exit the stage.

MC: When I fly at half-mast to honor those who served, I weep when I lie in the trembling arms of a grieving relative at the graveside of their fallen loved one. *[Pause]*

I bear witness to all of America's finest hours. But MY finest hour comes when we stand side by side as members of one unified Nation.

Retiree completes a Right Face and returns to his original position.

MC: It is the freedom that we fiercely defend and your love of this Nation that keeps me standing tall. I will not wither, I will not fall. I will not lay down the trust you have placed in me. *[Pause]*

I am bold. I am proud. My name is OLD GLORY. God Bless America. Long may I wave. *[Pause]*

MC: Ladies and gentlemen, you have just witnessed the Old Glory Ceremony. Please join us in a round of applause for our retiring officer.

MC leads applause.

Military Funeral Honors

The provision of Military Funeral Honors is based on custom and tradition. The ceremony is carried out with dignity and respect, as a display of the Nation's gratitude for those men and women who have served our Country. Burial in a national cemetery, other than Arlington National Cemetery, is provided to PHS officers who die on active duty or who served on active duty and were separated under other than dishonorable conditions. Military Funeral Honors for PHS decedents may be provided at the time of burial by the U.S. Coast Guard [Source: Military Funeral Honors, DoD Website, 2013].

Elements of the Ceremony
The military funeral has certain basic elements that are common to all such ceremonies. For eligible *veterans*, the core elements of the funeral honors ceremony will be performed, consisting of the ceremonial folding and presentation of the American flag and sounding of Taps (bugler or a quality recording). At least two uniformed service persons and a bugler, if available, shall perform the ceremony. One of the uniformed personnel is a representative of the Public Health Service and shall present the flag to the chaplain or family, as appropriate. Uniformed services are encouraged to provide additional elements of honors as personnel and resources permit.

For members who die while on *active duty* and *retired officers*, additional elements of honors may be provided if personnel and resources are available, including an officer-in-charge (OIC, who may be the officer representing the PHS), six uniformed body bearers (casket team), a seven-person firing detail and a bugler. Funeral honors can be efficiently rendered by a detail of the OIC and eight service members, who serve as both the body bearers and firing detail. For retirees and veterans, the member's minister, priest or rabbi will normally officiate at funeral services.

Up to eight honorary pallbearers, civilians and/or uniformed service members, may be selected by family of the deceased. Honorary pallbearers form two facing ranks, such that the casket is carried between the two ranks when it is brought into and out of a chapel, and when the casket is moved from the hearse (caisson at Arlington National Cemetery) to the burial plot. When marching, the honorary pallbearers form two columns.

Flag. A U.S. flag is provided for the burial service of service members and veterans. The flag for those who die on active duty is provided by the PHS, and the flag for veterans is provided by the Department of Veterans Affairs.

When used to cover the casket, the flag is placed with the union at the head and over the left shoulder of the deceased. The flag should not touch the ground and it is not lowered into the grave.

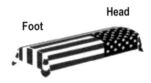

Head

Foot

Sequence of Events

Chapel. The general sequence of full or standard Military Funeral Honors, beginning with a chapel service, is as follows.

- The immediate family, relatives and friends of the deceased are seated in the right front pews of the chapel before the casket is carried in.
- The honorary pallbearers take positions in two facing ranks in front of the chapel entrance before the hearse arrives. Upon arrival, honorary pallbearers in uniform render the hand salute and those who are in civilian clothing place the right hand over their heart, when the body bearers remove the casket from the hearse.
- The body bearers then carry the casket, foot end first (reverse for a chaplain's funeral), between the two ranks. The honorary pallbearers come to the order and fall in behind the casket as it is carried into the chapel. In the chapel, the honorary pallbearers take places in the left front pews and the casket team in the rear pews (see illustration below).

Chapel Formation

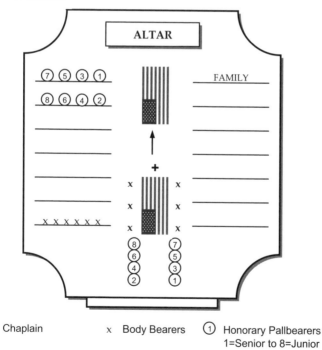

+ Chaplain   x Body Bearers   ① Honorary Pallbearers
                                             1=Senior to 8=Junior

- *Note that in the Catholic Church, the American flag that drapes the casket is respectfully removed and the casket brought into the chapel draped with a pall (a white cloth symbolizing baptism). When the religious ceremony has ended, the pall is removed and the flag is replaced on the casket, where it remains to the gravesite.*

- After the chapel service, the reverse order is followed: led by the chaplain/clergyman, the honorary pallbearers precede the casket in two columns and, just outside the chapel entrance, form two facing ranks between which the casket is carried by the casket team to the hearse.

Graveside Service. The general sequence of Military Funeral Honors at the cemetery is as follows.

- Upon reaching the gravesite, the chaplain, followed by the OIC and body bearers carrying the casket, leads the way to the grave through the ranks of honorary pallbearers, followed by the family and other mourners.
- The casket is placed over the grave and the casket team holds the flag, stretched taut and level, waist high over the casket during the service.
- After the committal service is read by the chaplain/clergyman, the OIC calls to "Present Arms." Everyone in attendance should stand during the uniformed service Honors. The rifle volleys are fired and, at the conclusion of the third volley, the bugler sounds Taps.
- After Taps, the flag is folded by the casket team, and the head body bearer passes the flag to the OIC, salutes, and the casket team departs.
- The OIC holds the flag with the right hand supporting the bottom and the left hand placed on top, and stands holding the folded flag with the straight edge facing the recipient. The OIC leans forward and solemnly presents the flag to the family. The OIC may also hand the flag to a uniformed service chaplain who then presents it to the family. The flag is presented with traditional condolences. In 2012, the Department of Defense standardized the presentation wording, as follows:

  "On behalf of the President of the United States, the United States Public Health Service [uniformed service name], and a grateful Nation, please accept this flag as a symbol of our appreciation for your loved one's honorable and faithful service."

The OIC then offers condolences to other mourners seated in the front row.

Cremains. The funeral service is conducted in the same manner. A body bearer will hand carry the receptacle containing cremated remains, with the folded flag carried by a flag bearer on the flag's own right. The folded flag is placed next to the receptacle when on a stand. At the grave or columbarium, the body bearers unfold the flag and hold it taut over the urn of cremains during the service.

Uniformed Service Attire and Salutes

Uniformed personnel attending in an official or unofficial capacity should wear the Service Dress uniform. Render the hand salute at any time when the caisson or hearse arrives, when the casket is being moved, during the firing of the volley, while Taps is being sounded, and while the casket is being lowered into the grave.

CHAPTER FIVE

SOCIAL CEREMONY PROTOCOL

Commissioned officers will, at various times throughout their career, plan and participate in uniformed service social functions. These formal events are important in building a sense of community within the service. Social activities, whether associated with a uniformed service or civilian life, provide a social fabric that helps to bond people in friendship. In this chapter, those social activities that have evolved from, and relate to military life are discussed. These functions are based on custom and tradition, and it is important that officers familiarize themselves with the basic protocol of such events.

DINING-IN & DINING-OUT
OFFICIAL DINNERS & RECEPTIONS
MILITARY WEDDING CEREMONY

Dining-In & Dining-Out

The dining-in and dining-out are formal dinners that are a tradition in all of the uniformed services. It is thought that dining-in had its inception in antiquity, beginning with the early Roman legions, Vikings, and English knights who held great feasts to celebrate victories in battle and individual feats of heroism. Formalized dining-in is also thought to have been a practice in old English monastic life. The monks, as educators, spread the custom to universities where graduates, who later became British officers, may have carried the tradition to the military. The British instituted customs and rules for the "mess night", which was adopted by the early Continental Army and Navy of the U.S., and slowly took hold within the U.S. armed services. While often used for special occasions such as welcoming new officers or recognizing a dignitary, these ceremonial dinners are primarily a social occasion to pay tribute, and promote good fellowship and camaraderie among officers.

Dining-In
The dining-in as practiced in the Navy and Air Force is also known as mess night in the Marine Corps and Coast Guard, and regimental dinner in the Army. A dining-in is held by a military unit or organization for its own officers only, with the possible exception of the guest of honor. For many years, it was considered a command function at which all officers of the command were expected to be present. In recent years, attendance at the dining-in is encouraged and often deemed voluntary.

Dining-Out
The dining-out is similar to dining-in, but is inclusive of service members' spouses, personal guests and invited members of other uniformed services. Officers of the sponsoring unit are the "members of the mess," and all others attend by invitation. Dining-in/dining-out, hereinafter referred to as dining-out, are formal events that are at the same time intended to be spirited and enjoyed by all participants.

Dress
Active duty dress for the occasion is the Dinner Dress Blue Jacket or Dinner Dress White Jacket, without gloves. Officers with the rank of Lieutenant Commander and below may wear Dinner Dress Blue or Dinner Dress White (Service Dress Blue/White with black bow tie and miniature medals, no name tag). Civilian dress is formal – black tie tuxedo or dark business suit for men, and evening gown without gloves for women.

Elements
The format and program sequence of the dining-out varies among services, but the PHS tends to follow the Navy model with modifications. The dining-out is planned well in advance to ensure a successful program. Principal elements of the function include a formal setting such as the officers' club or restaurant with a separate room, a fine dinner with formal place settings, the presence of honored guests, traditional toasts, and camaraderie of members.

Officers of the Mess. The dining-out has two Officers: a presiding senior officer or president, assisted by an officer serving in the capacity of a vice-president called "Mister/Madam Vice" (or, "the Vice"). Mr. Vice is normally a junior officer with a keen wit and entertaining style. He is the only person allowed to speak without the president's leave. In addition, the occasion usually has an honored guest who is an official guest seated to the right of the president. The president, honored/distinguished guests and spouses sit at a head table facing the attendees, with the president seated at the center. Mr. Vice sits at a small table away from the head table, where he can view the president and also observe the entire room. The president uses a gavel to direct attendees, as follows: one rap means to be seated, two raps mean to rise and stand in place, and three raps mean that the attention of members is needed.

Reception

The pre-dinner reception allows members and guests to meet one another, and provides an opportunity to greet the official guests and senior officers. It is important that members and their guests arrive on time for this activity which is considered integral to the event purpose. If the dinner has assigned seating, a seating chart will be posted near the reception area for viewing.

Note that from this point forward, the inclusion and sequence of events can be arranged in a way that is most appropriate for the program. [For further information, see OPNAVINST 1710.7A, 15 June 2001, and other relevant documents.]

Dinner

When it is time for the dinner, a chime is sounded or a bagpiper, if available, plays marching music and leads the group into the mess (dining area). Members and guests should dispose of their drinks and proceed to the mess. Diners stand quietly behind their chairs, at which time the head table officers and official guests enter. When those at the head table are in place, the music ceases. The president calls the mess to order and directs the Surgeon General's Honor Cadre. The USPHS Music Ensemble leads the group in singing the national anthem and the PHS March. A member will offer grace, and the president then invites everyone to be seated with one rap of the gavel. The president will at this time make opening remarks, to include welcoming guests of the mess and introducing the guest of honor and principal officers of the event. Dinner commences after the following two rituals are accomplished.

Inspection of the Beef. The piper will play "Roast Beef of Olde England" as the president or other designee marches over to sample the beef entrée. If acceptable, the president/designee announces to the diners that the beef is tasty and fit for human consumption.

Grog/Punchbowl Ceremony. The president or designee will next describe for diners the flavorful (nonalcoholic) ingredients of the grog. The grog may be premixed, or ceremoniously prepared in the Grog Bowl.

If buffet style, diners will be directed by the president to proceed to the buffet table. Officers and their guests should then thoroughly enjoy the sumptuous meal and amicable conversation with their table partners.

Social Activity/Mess Rule Violations

The organizers of a dining-out will prepare "Rules of the Mess," which are laced with humor and included in the printed program. Once the dinner begins, penalties will be levied for violations of rules of the mess. Mr. Vice will read the list of offenders, and members are also encouraged to note violations by other members of the mess. This is done by raising a point of order with Mr. Vice. The member stands, stating "Mr. Vice, a point of order." Mr. Vice responds with "Sir/Madam, state your point of order." The president or Mr. Vice may allow an accused offender the opportunity to rebut the charges, and will render a judgment on the validity of the charge. Infractions are noted and penalties levied for said offenses. The usual penalty is a small fine, the proceeds of which are sent to a charity or used for a special purpose. A member who is in violation of the rules must pay the fine and is obliged to drink from the grog bowl. Upon reaching the grog bowl, the member must salute the president, fill a cup, toast the mess ("To the Mess"), drain the contents of the cup, invert the cup over his/her head to signify that it is empty, and again salute the president before returning to his/her seat.

Rules of the Mess

The following is the list of customary rules, with some modifications, under which the mess may be conducted. They are designed to conform to tradition and promote levity. Violators are subject to the wrath and mischievousness of the Vice. All assigned penalties will be carried out before the membership.

1. Thou shalt not be late for the appointed hour.
2. Thou shalt make every effort to the meet all guests.
3. Thou shalt move to the mess when thee hear the chimes and remain standing until seated by the President.
4. Thou shalt not bring drinks into the mess.
5. Thou shalt not smoke – the smoking lamp is permanently extinguished.
6. Thou shalt not leave the mess whilst convened. Military protocol overrides all calls of nature (*unless essential and permission is received*).
7. Thou shalt participate in all toasts unless thyself or thy group is being honored with a toast.
8. Thou shalt ensure that thy glass is always charged while toasting.
9. Thou shalt keep toasts and comments within the limits of good taste and mutual respect. Degrading or insulting remarks will be frowned upon by the membership. However, good-natured needling is encouraged.
10. Thou shalt not murder the Queen's English.
11. Thou shalt always use the proper toasting procedure.
12. Thou shalt fall into disrepute with thy peers if the pleats of thy cummerbund are inverted.
13. Thou shalt also be painfully regarded if thy bow tie rides at an obvious list.
14. Thou shalt consume thy meal in a manner becoming a gentleperson.
15. Thou shalt not laugh at ridiculously funny comments unless the President first shows approval by laughing.
16. Thou shalt not question the decisions of the President.
17. When the mess opens or adjourns, thou shalt rise and wait for the members at the head table to take their places or depart.
18. Thou shalt not begin eating a course of the meal before members of the head table.
19. Thou shalt not engage in verbal discourse whilst another member has the floor.
20. Thou shalt enjoy thyself to the fullest.

Recess

When the dinner is finished, the president raps the gavel three times to get everyone's attention, and announces a short recess for participants to refresh themselves and to allow the wait staff to remove all dishes, flatware and glasses. The gavel is then rapped twice, indicating that members should stand and wait by their chairs until the head table has departed. This also signals that the program relating to rule violations is concluded.

When the recess is over, members will be led by the piper back to the mess, where they should remain standing behind their chairs until the head table has made their entry and the president invites everyone to be seated.

Wine Pouring

If formal and informal toasts are on the program at this time, the wait staff will place wine glasses and decanters of wine (port wine is traditional) on the dining tables. Each person fills his/her own glass with wine. By custom, the decanter is passed to the right around the table, without touching the table, until all glasses are filled (charged). The most junior officer at each table is responsible for ensuring that all glasses are charged. Those who prefer not to drink an alcoholic beverage can choose to fill their glass with wine, raise it, but not sip from it during the toast, or they may drink a nonalcoholic beverage (e.g., cider; *not* soda) with which to toast.

Toasting

Formal and informal toasts may be offered prior to (with white entrée wine) or after the dinner (preferably with port wine).

Formal. The president begins with formal toasts to the offices/positions held by high ranking officials (by title, *not* individual's name), honored guests, and to institutions. Traditionally, the president proposes the first toast, which may be to "To the Colors". In order of precedence, he/she offers a toast "To the Commander in Chief" or "To the President of the United States", known as the Loyalty Toast, to which all stand and respond "To the President." The mess president, vice president or designated member may next toast the HHS Secretary and the Surgeon General. For example, the president will state, "To the Surgeon General of the United States." Mr. Vice stands and seconds the toast, "Gentlemen, Ladies, the Surgeon General of the United States." Diners stand (civilian women guests may remain seated), repeat the toast in unison, "The Surgeon General" while raising their glasses, and take a sip of wine.

Thereafter, the president may recognize members who offer prearranged formal toasts, including, for example, toasts to the USPHS professional categories. The member stands, stating "Mr. Vice, I am (*rank, name*) and would like to propose a toast." The Vice recognizes the member by stating "The mess recognizes (*rank, name*)." The member responds with "I propose a toast

to the (*professional category*)." Protocol is that a toast by the president is seconded by Mr. Vice, and a toast by a member is seconded by the president.

Informal. The president then will invite members of the mess to offer informal toasts – these may be humorous (in good taste). An officer must rise and
first request to propose a toast from Mr. Vice. When recognized, the officer
proceeds with the toast. If deemed suitable, the president seconds the toast.
All present should respond to this and subsequent toasts with "Hear, Hear!"

Honored Guest Address

The president reintroduces the guest of honor, who will address the group for
about 10 to 15 minutes on a topic that is entertaining or uplifting and consistent with the intent of the dining-out. Following the address, Mr. Vice should
propose a toast to "our distinguished speaker."

Cake Ceremony

In the PHS, a cake (preferably bearing the USPHS logo), after being properly
inspected, is cut with a PHS sword by the president or honored guest (if
senior) and the most junior officer present and served to all attendees.

Concluding Activities

The president will conclude the evening with a formal toast to the U.S. Public
Health Service. Mr. Vice faces the mess and seconds the toast. All present
rise, repeat the toast in unison, "The United States Public Health Service," and
completely drain their glasses. Everyone should remain standing at their
places while the PHS March music is played. The president may propose a
final toast of the evening to fallen uniformed service comrades, which is performed with water. He will then thank the guest of honor and other guests
for their attendance and key organizers of the event. Those at the head table
will then depart the mess, followed by members and guests.

POW/MIA/Fallen Comrade Table

By tradition, a small, round table covered with a white tablecloth and an
empty chair are placed at the front of the room to honor POW/MIAs/fallen
uniformed service members. On top of the table are specified items, each of
which carries a symbolic meaning (OPNAVINST 1710.7A).

The small table symbolizes the frailty of one prisoner alone; the white tablecloth represents the purity of their response to our Country's call to arms; the empty chair
depicts those who are not present; round table shows that our concern for them
is never ending; the Bible represents faith in a higher power and the pledge of our
Country; the black napkin stands for the emptiness of these warriors in the hearts
of their families and friends; single red rose reminds us of their families and loved
ones, and the red ribbon the love of our Country; yellow candle and ribbon sym-
bolize the everlasting hope for a joyous reunion; slices of lemon and salt on the
bread plate remind us of their bitter fate, and the tears of their families, respectively; and, the wine glass turned upside down reminds us that our distinguished
comrades cannot be with us to drink a toast and join in the festivities.

Planning

Planning and preparations for a dining-out should begin three to four months in advance of the event date. For those officers tasked with planning the dining-out, a planning checklist is provided in Appendix B.

There are various program formats used for the dining-out, two examples of which are provided below. Note that not all items must be in the program for a successful event. The program can be modified to best accommodate the requirements (e.g., facility, resources, time) of the sponsoring group.

SEQUENCE A	SEQUENCE B
RECEPTION	RECEPTION
MOVE TO THE MESS	MOVE TO THE MESS
MESS CALLED TO ORDER	MESS CALLED TO ORDER
INVOCATION	INVOCATION
WELCOME AND INTRODUCTIONS	WELCOME AND INTRODUCTIONS
INSPECTION OF THE BEEF	FORMAL TOASTS
GROG CEREMONY	GROG CEREMONY
DINNER	INSPECTION OF THE BEEF
SOCIAL ACTIVITY	DINNER
RECESS	SOCIAL ACTIVITY
WINE POURING	RECESS
FORMAL TOASTS	DESSERT
GUEST SPEAKER	GUEST SPEAKER
CAKE CEREMONY	CLOSING REMARKS
CLOSING REMARKS	

Official Dinners & Receptions

The military services have traditionally been strongly supportive of social functions as a way to enhance the lives of its members. These occasions build a sense of community, and are important because officers and their families are often assigned to a duty station for relatively few years without sufficient time to build an outside social network, and/or they may be at a remote duty station or live on a military base where civilian socializing is limited.

Official social functions range from informal to formal affairs. Less formal occasions include functions such as cocktail parties with appetizers and drinks, and "hails and farewells" with various formats to welcome newcomers and bid farewell to those leaving a duty station. Formal dinners and receptions are usually held to honor someone or mark a special occasion. Truly formal events that call for engraved invitations are infrequent.

All of the military services hold official receptions and dinners (buffet or formal), including celebrating their annual Birthday Ball at various venues throughout the Nation. The PHS Commissioned Officers Foundation (COF), in cooperation with the OSG, sponsors the annual Anchor and Caduceus (A&C) Dinner, which features the C. Everett Koop Memorial Lecture. A&C Dinners are also held at various regional locales, sponsored by a Branch of the Commissioned Officers Association. And, there are PHS Category Luncheons held each year at the COF Scientific and Training Symposium.

All uniformed service officers are expected to know social etiquette and have good manners. Officers will have occasion to attend these functions and may also participate in planning such an event. The following information covers those topics which may pertain to semi-formal and formal events.

BASICS

Some basic guidance is provided for those attending receptions and dinners.

Be on Time. Receptions and formal dinners are important social functions in the uniformed services, and service members and their guests should be punctual. For receptions, one should arrive within 20 minutes of the starting time and, if there is a receiving line, with sufficient time to greet dignitaries in the receiving line. For formal dinners, it is essential to arrive on time and preferably before the starting time.

Consuming Beverages, Food. Always use a cocktail napkin with iced drinks to contain drips and avoid presenting a cold, wet handshake. Most importantly, consume alcoholic drinks in moderation. When hors d'oeuvres and buffet-style food are served, do not linger around the buffet table for long periods of time, so as not to give the appearance of monopolizing the bounty of food. Once your food is obtained, move away from the immediate area to allow others easy access to the table.

Conversation. Topics of discussion at a social function or reception should generally be kept light. Senior officers should make an effort to converse with junior officers, including those not known. When at the dining table, it is important to talk with those who are seated on both sides of you.

Departures. It is no longer improper to leave before a guest of honor, but it is important to greet an honored guest or ranking official before leaving.

Seating. Seating at formal dinners may be assigned or by order of precedence. Ensure that seating is not prearranged before taking your place. Due deference should be given by junior officers to those more senior, allowing senior officers to sit at preferred locations at the table, if applicable.

INVITATIONS

Generally, invitations are extended about three to four weeks before the event. Invitations to large or important affairs, or to functions planned during a holiday season, should be sent at least one month in advance.

Types and Content of Invitations. There are several accepted ways to extend an invitation. For informal and semi-formal occasions, invitations may be extended in person; by telephone; e-mail for large, informal gatherings; "fill-in" preprinted card; handwritten card; or by a printed card. For formal occasions, invitations may be extended by telephone, followed by a "To Remind" card; handwritten card; printed or thermographed (raised print) card; or by engraved card. An engraved card is used only for the most formal occasions, with white or cream color cardstock and matching envelopes.

All written invitations should contain complete information about the function. When the occasion calls for a printed or engraved invitation, the text is normally written in the third person. Information is usually centered and, starting at the top, includes the following (see *Sample Invitation,* next page):

- **Who** – The host of the function, either organization or individual. Ranks and names are written in full. For very high ranking officials, the position title is used (e.g., The Surgeon General). An admiral's flag may be centered at the top or the upper left corner of his/her invitations. Follow with a phrase such as "cordially invites you" or, when also intended for one's spouse, use the phrase "requests the pleasure of your company."
- **What** – The type of function, such as "at a reception." If more than one activity is planned, indicate that here or in the lower right corner.
- **Why** – The purpose, such as "in honor of (*specify*)."
- **When** – The day, date of the week and time; the day, date (no year) and hour are spelled out, with the day and month capitalized.
- **Where** – The name and address of the venue and, if applicable, the name of the banquet or meeting room.
- **Dress** – If not evident from the event, the dress code is provided in the lower right corner.

- *How to Reply* – RSVP is the abbreviation for répondez s'il vous plaît, meaning *please reply*. The RSVP is located in the lower left corner of the invitation and will include the contact information. The invitation may also specify "Regrets Only." Alternatively, an RSVP card and self-addressed return envelope may be enclosed.

Mailing Invitations. Invitations are inserted into the envelope so that the text faces the back side of the envelope and the top coincides with the top of the envelope. Secondary materials, such as an RSVP card, are placed behind the invitation (or inside a double fold invitation) within the envelope. Envelope addresses may be typed or handwritten (do not use labels). For formal events, envelopes should only be handwritten in black ink.

Replies. Respond promptly regarding your acceptance of an invitation; normally, this should be done within 48 hours of receiving an invitation.

Canceling an Acceptance. There are few acceptable reasons for not showing or canceling after accepting an invitation. A cancellation of your initial acceptance should be briefly explained, with a sincere apology. Telephone the cancellation as soon as possible and, for very important functions, follow-up with a written note.

Sample Invitation

The PHS Commissioned Officers
Foundation

requests the pleasure of your company
at a dinner
in honor of

The Surgeon General of the United States

on Saturday, the fifteenth of July
at eight o'clock

The Naval Officers' Club
Bethesda, Maryland

RSVP
(301) 555-4000

Reception, 7:00 P.M.
Service Dress Blue

ORDER OF PRECEDENCE

In official interactions and at ceremonial and social occasions, deferential respect may be given to the position that an individual holds. Such positions are prioritized according to society's perception of the importance of that office. Protocol governs the precedence given to positions in government, ecclesiastical and diplomatic life. In the U.S. government, such official positions are attained through election or appointment to an office, or by promotion within a uniformed service.

Official positions in the government are assigned relative levels of importance, with the President holding the highest level of precedence. The official precedence lists do not cover all positions, in which situation precedence is determined by the consideration of an individual's prominence within their organization and career field. Diplomatic precedence is set by international agreement dating from the Congress of Vienna in 1815, and includes other criteria such as the date that diplomats present their credentials.

The military is very evident in the application of precedence according to grade. By custom, uniformed service officers of the same grade are ranked by date of rank; if the dates of rank are the same, then by total active service date and, if the same, officers in the Regular Corps take precedence among themselves according to their position on the permanent promotion list. Active duty officers precede Reserve officers, and Reserve officers precede retired officers of the same rank. In a ceremonial or social setting, a spouse is generally accorded the same ranking as the principal to whom precedence is given. In the PHS, considerations of precedence are usually limited to an individual's service rank. Officers should nonetheless be cognizant of the precedence code, particularly when high ranking military officers are in attendance at official functions.

RECEPTIONS/RECEIVING LINE

Receptions are a customary form of official entertaining, and often include a receiving line to afford those in attendance an opportunity to meet and greet the host and honored guest. It is typically held for about 30 minutes, and up to 45 minutes in duration for large receptions.

The receiving line should be in a location that does not disrupt guest flow to the reception area. A table may be placed behind the official party in the receiving line for water. Flags are arranged behind the table in order of precedence: the U.S. flag at the position of honor (i.e., the flag's own right), followed by Departmental and/or organizational flag, and then an admiral's flag. There are no firm rules for the formation of receiving lines, other than the host and honored guest position themselves at the head of the line, with spouses on their left, and all other officers are arrayed to the left in single file in order of rank.

An announcer may be at the head of the receiving line to receive the names of each guest/couple in the waiting line. The announcer normally is an aide or other officer. The announcer introduces the guest to the host who, in turn, presents the guest to the guest of honor. Sometimes a "set-up" aide will be stationed several feet before the receiving line to give directions to those waiting in line. A male officer may be positioned at the end of a receiving line to avoid leaving a woman there. At large receptions, an officer may be positioned just off the end of the receiving line to direct guests to the main reception area. For official receptions, the customary order is a follows.

[Aide] ~ Host ~ Host's Spouse ~ Guest of Honor ~ Honored Guest's Spouse

or

[Aide] ~ Host ~ Guest of Honor ~ Honored Guest's Spouse ~ Host's Spouse

When the guest of honor is a head of state, the line is rearranged as follows:

[Aide] ~ Chief of State ~ Chief of State's Spouse ~ Host ~ Host's Spouse

Guests in the waiting line arrange themselves in either of two ways: women precede men, as is traditional; or, officers/officials precede their spouses or guests – the latter arrangement is customary at official functions of the Air Force, Navy, and Marine Corps.

In either case, the officer uses his/her official title and name ("Captain Susan Carter and Mr. Carter"). If an aide is receiving names, guests do not greet or shake hands with the aide. Guests should avoid starting a conversation with the host or guest of honor but, if so, keep it brief. In proceeding down a lengthy receiving line, guests should simply offer their name, shake hands and greet each person in the receiving line with, for example, "Good evening" or "How do you do." Guests should never be holding a drink or food while meeting the official party in a receiving line.

DINNER SEATING ARRANGEMENTS

There are several seating arrangements that depend on the type and formality of the occasion and the guest composition. Two representative arrangements are the mixed dinner table and head/speaker's table. If a mixed dinner is held (Figure 1.), the host and hostess sit at the head and foot of the table. When the occasion is a large official dinner with long tables, the host and hostess move to the center of the lengthwise sides of the table.

All other guests are seated according to their rank. The senior ranking/-honored male guest is seated at the right of the hostess, and the senior ranking/honored female guest is at the right of the host. The second ranking man sits to the left of the hostess and the second ranking female sits to the host's left, and so on thereafter.

When precedence considerations are not essential, the host can modify the seating arrangement somewhat with the intent of creating an interesting mix of guests to enhance enjoyment at the dinner. Generally, guests are seated by alternating man and woman, which can be altered so that a woman is not seated at the end of a table.

HOST

	Ranking		
1	Woman	Woman	**2**
3	Man	Man	**4**
4	Woman	Woman	**3**
2	Man	Man	**1**

HOSTESS

Figure 1. Mixed Table

Figure 2. Head/Speakers Table

Note that a spouse is accorded the same rank as the principal (i.e., the person in who rank is vested). Thus, when a senior ranking man is seated to the right of the hostess, his wife will normally be seated to the right of the host if no senior ranking/honored female guest displaces her. If the spouse is also an officer or holds an official position with precedence ranking, that person is seated in accordance with his/her rank.

Whereas the place of honor is always to the right of the host/hostess, that position conveys to a senior ranking guest according to the rules of precedence. In order to allow an honored guest to be seated in the place of honor when a higher-ranking person is present, the host may want to ask the ranking guest to waive his seating right, if appropriate, or make the ranking guest a co-host of the event.

The seating protocol should be followed for formal dinners; however, officers will likely sit with their spouses at most occasions that are sponsored by the PHS and related organizations. For some occasions such as parties and retirements, spouses should be seated side-by-side. In these instances, the wife sits to the right of the husband, who assists with the wife's chair.

When being seated, diners should move to the right of the chair and sit from their left side. This will lessen the possibility of chairs or people bumping into one another.

TOASTING

Toasting originated in the sixteenth century with the English custom of adding a small piece of spiced toast to flavor wine, and the term came to be applied to a drink proposed in honor of a person. A toast to honor individuals or institutions lends special significance to an event. All guests should participate, allowing the host, a senior officer or the official who organized a dinner to make the first toast. This is typically done once the dessert is served and the wine or champagne glasses are filled (never use liqueur or a mixed drink). Nonalcoholic beverage drinkers may raise their empty or filled wine glass (if filled, they need not drink from it), or sip from a water-filled glass during the toast (note, however, that in some military messes it is considered highly improper to drink a toast with water). Water only is used by all participants for toasts that honor those who are missing in action, prisoners of war or fallen service members.

A toast should be relatively brief, relevant to the individual and always on a warm and laudatory note; an injection of humor may impart a "lift" to the toast, as well (note that formal and diplomatic toasts to an individual are made to that person's official position). The person making the toast should stand and project in a clear voice while raising his/her glass in a salute. At formal occasions, the toastmaster stands to propose the toast, and guests rise before or after to respond to the toast; non-active duty women may remain seated unless the host's wife rises. For less formal occasions, all guests can remain seated. At the conclusion of the toast, guests should turn and, looking at the person who was toasted, raise their glass; the person's position or name (as proper) may be repeated in unison and a sip of wine is then taken.

The person who is honored remains seated and does not drink to the toast, but should nod in acknowledgment. After the toast, he/she may rise to offer a toast with words of thanks.

Planning

Planning for a formal reception should begin two to three months in advance of the event date. For those officers tasked with planning a reception, a planning checklist is provided in Appendix C.

Military Wedding Ceremony

A military wedding provides special pageantry to the marriage ceremony. In most respects, the military wedding is much like civilian weddings, in that the ceremony itself is religious. What distinguishes the military wedding and makes it particularly memorable are the uniforms and uniformed service customs. Principal features include the following.

Uniforms

The groom and/or bride, if a uniformed service member, may wear the uniform; ceremonial or dinner dress uniforms are worn. The bride, if a PHS officer, may choose to instead wear a more traditional wedding dress. The bridesmaids wear formal dresses. Members of different service branches may be included in the wedding party, but all should wear the equivalent uniform as the groom and/or bride. Note that a boutonniere is not worn on a uniform.

Arch of Swords

A popular military tradition is for the newly married couple to end the ceremony by passing under an archway of swords (sabers in the Army, Marine Corps and Air Force). Alternatively, the arch of swords may be performed at the reception, just prior to the cake-cutting ceremony. If swords are unavailable, an honor cordon can be formed to render courtesy hand salutes. The arch of swords is an old English and American custom that is a symbolic pledge of loyalty from the uniformed service to the newly married couple; thus, only the newlyweds transit the arch.

It is traditional that swords are never unsheathed in a chapel, so the arch normally takes place outside the chapel or church. With the chaplain's permission (e.g., in the event of inclement weather), the arch may be formed inside at the rear of the chapel near or in the vestibule. Only commissioned personnel in proper uniform, with gloves, participate in the arch of swords. Those officers serving as groomsmen and/or ushers may form the sword detail, supplemented by other officers, as needed, to complete a six or eight member group. The sword detail forms at the bottom of the chapel steps, in two equal facing ranks, with sufficient room for the bride and groom to pass.

Following the vows, the newlyweds lead the recessional and, upon reaching the vestibule, wait in a secluded area. After the guests have left the chapel and are ready to observe the ceremony, the bride and groom emerge and stand outside the main entrance. The best man announces the new couple to those assembled, "Ladies and gentlemen, may I present Mr. (or rank) and Mrs. (or rank) (*surname*)." The officer in charge (OIC) of the sword detail then commands, "Officers, draw swords," and the swords are drawn from their scabbards in one continuous motion, with arms fully extended, to an angle of 45-degrees, rising so that the tips touch the opposite swords, and ensuring that the cutting edge is up. The couple slowly walks under the arch of swords until they reach the last two sword bearers, where they pause. The officers slowly lower and cross their swords in front of the couple, detaining them momentarily. The sword bearer on the right may give the bride a gentle "swat" on the rear with the sword and say, "Welcome to the U.S. Public Health Service!" Note that this step is omitted if the bride is a member of the USPHS. The couple may kiss, the swords are slowly raised, and the couple completes their passage. The OIC then gives the command of "Return swords." (Military Source: Marine Corps Order P5060.20, The Marine Corps Drill and Ceremonies Manual, 05 May 2003.)

In the Chapel
Military couples may want an American and/or service flag posted in the chapel and possibly service music, such as the service song, played during the recessional, noting that permission may be needed from the chaplain. With regard to reserved seating, as you face the altar, the bride's family is traditionally seated in the front left pews and the groom's family in the front right pews. Invited flag officers and official VIPs may be seated in pews just behind the immediate families.

Reception
At the reception, the national colors and distinguishing flags may be displayed, centered behind the receiving line. Decorations may be patriotic or service-themed, such as the colors of the USPHS. Mini-sized flags may be placed as centerpieces at the tables, and the service song played among the music selections during the reception. At a formal reception, military guests are seated together by rank. However, PHS officers will likely prefer to sit with family members rather than together at one table.

A highlight is cutting the cake with the groom's sword. The bride, standing left of the groom, receives and holds the sword by the hilt with her right hand. The groom rests his right hand over hers, and places his left arm around his bride, and together they cut the first piece of wedding cake. A server places the slice of cake on a plate and hands a fork to each of the couple, who then carefully serve each other a small bite.

Planning
The military wedding can be held in a military chapel, civilian church or other location. If the marriage ceremony is held at a military chapel, the chaplain can provide information regarding many aspects of the occasion, possibly including vendors for the ceremony and reception, such as a wedding planner, florist and photographer. The chaplain can also provide assistance in arranging for a civilian clergy member to officiate or assist in the ceremony at the military chapel. While military chaplains perform the marriage ceremony at no charge, it is customary for the couple to make a donation to the chapel fund in appreciation for the service rendered.

CHAPTER SIX

SPECIAL DUTY POSITIONS

The USPHS provides opportunities to serve the Commissioned Corps in special duty positions that will enrich an officer's career experience. Officers should consider becoming involved in these special assignments, which are personally fulfilling and build camaraderie and esprit de corps within the Corps.

AIDE-DE-CAMP
ESCORT OFFICER
SERVICE BOARDS
CHIEF PROFESSIONAL OFFICER
HONOR CADRE
JUNIOR OFFICER ADVISORY GROUP
LIAISON, COMMISSIONED CORPS
MINORITY OFFICERS LIAISON COUNCIL
MUSIC ENSEMBLE
PROFESSIONAL ADVISORY COMMITTEE
PROTOCOL OFFICER
READINESS FORCE
SURGEON GENERAL'S POLICY ADVISORY COUNCIL

Aide-de-Camp & Escort Officer

Aide-de-Camp

The **aide-de-camp** (French: *camp assistant*) is a PHS officer who acts in the capacity of a fulltime or temporary duty confidential assistant to a flag officer – one who carries the rank of Admiral at grade 0-7 and above. The role of military aide was adopted from the European tradition during the American Revolution, beginning with those who served as aides to General George Washington. Aides are often selected for their leadership abilities, and they have played a significant part in American military history. It is a mark of distinction to serve as an aide and it presents a rare opportunity to observe senior officers in positions of leadership. It is well known that a substantial proportion of military aides go on to become leaders in their own right.

The aide-de-camp (ADC) provides administrative support and performs a range of assistive duties. The aide is called upon as a ready resource to relieve high-ranking civilian and uniformed service officials (hereinafter referred to as "the principal") of everyday matters. The HHS Secretary, Deputy and Assistant Secretaries, Surgeon General, Deputy Surgeon General, and other flag officers may have the services of an aide. See also the Sections on *Escort Officer* and *Protocol Officer* for further information, and Appendix D. for a travel planning form.

An **escort officer** refers to the local officer who is temporarily assigned to meet and accompany the principal who is arriving from out-of-town, and may serve as the aide-de-camp if the principal's regular aide is absent. The escort officer may work in tandem with a principal's aide-de-camp and staff to brief and provide guidance to the principal, and secure ground transportation, as needed, to accommodate the official's itinerary. The escort officer might also coordinate actions with a protocol officer when the visit is to a military command. See the Section, *Escort Officer,* below.

A **protocol officer** refers to an officer or civilian who provides fulltime management and support service to commanders with respect to travel, conferences, recognition programs, special ceremonies, social functions, and visits by distinguished visitors. The protocol officer also advises the commander and staff on military customs and courtesies, history, organization and policy. Escort officers will be coordinating a principal's visit with the protocol officer when one is present. See the Section, *Protocol Officer,* for more detailed information.

Qualifications

Those who serve as an aide should have certain basic qualifications. The ADC must first meet all professional, medical and fitness standards.

Knowledge and Communication. The PHS aide must have a comprehensive knowledgeable of uniformed service customs, courtesy, protocol, and social etiquette, to include making proper introductions. It is important that the aide have a good understanding of the U.S. Public Health Service – its history and mission, and familiarity with the agencies to which PHS officers are assigned. He/she has a thorough knowledge of service uniforms and their components. The aide is articulate and skilled in both verbal and written communications. And, the aide is able to identify, and takes the initiative to learn information that is personally deficient and needed for the proper performance of duties.

Personal Qualities. An aide must be self-reliant and resourceful. He is able to organize, prioritize and carry out assigned duties competently, with little or no guidance; this should not, however, preclude the aide from asking when uncertain. The ability to make sound judgments in the absence of specific instruction is vital. The aide has exceptional interpersonal skills, and is adept at dealing appropriately with people at all organizational levels.

Because his actions reflect directly upon the principal who chose him, it is imperative that the aide conduct his official duties responsibly. The aide must have integrity and convey professionalism in order to earn the respect of the principal and others with whom the aide interacts.

Dress and Grooming. The ADC must have an exemplary uniformed service appearance and bearing. An aide's grooming and dress should be impeccable. The aide should always maintain superior grooming standards, to include hair that is clean, trimmed and neatly styled; nails trimmed; good oral hygiene; and, for males, facial hair is clean-shaven. Use cologne/perfume very sparingly, if at all. Jewelry should be conservative and minimal, and personal articles such as pens and combs kept so they are not visible.

An aide's wardrobe, which may be necessarily extensive, must fit well and be clean, pressed, and maintained in conformance with all uniform standards. A secure knowledge of the proper dress and uniform components used for different occasions is essential, both for himself and when he may be called upon to advise the principal. The ADC must always be prepared for any occasion that requires the appropriate uniform.

Aiguillette. The PHS aide's uniform is distinguished by the wearing of an aiguillette on the left shoulder. The aiguillette signifies the official position of the wearer and provides an assurance of cooperation by others. The number of loops that comprise the aiguillette signify the rank of the principal, as follows: two loops, RADM; three loops, VADM; and four loops, 4-star ADM and those deemed equivalent or above (e.g., HHS Secretary, Deputy/Assistant Secretary).

Carrying Out Responsibilities
The ADC must subordinate his own desires to the needs of the principal. In this regard, the aide should take time to become acquainted with the principal's work habits, interests and preferences. In that way, he will achieve the principal's confidence and trust in his ability to make appropriate decisions.

It is essential that the aide maintain confidentiality with respect to discussions between the principal and others, and be circumspect regarding anything said or done by the principal that is not meant to be publicly disclosed.

The aide understands that fraternization with the principal is not allowed when the public and subordinates are present. The ADC is not to alter the requirement for a professional manner and adherence to uniformed service protocol while in public view. He should also be mindful that his official relationship with the principal does not confer command status. His demeanor must always conform to that which is expected of a subordinate, and show the proper respect accorded to ranking officers.

Duties

Administrative. The aide-de-camp is responsible for a multitude of tasks, some of which may be shared with other personnel such as the principal's secretarial and support staff. The scope of the aide's duties will also vary depending on the needs of the principal to whom assigned. The aide is responsible for administrative matters that may include scheduling, monitoring appointments, handling correspondence, carrying messages on behalf of the principal, vetting requests for the principal's time, serving at the start of a receiving line to introduce guests to the principal, and advising the principal on rules of protocol and etiquette. The aide will also be responsible for planning and coordinating the principal's participation at official ceremonies and meetings, and for briefing the principal on all relevant matters that pertain to such participation.

Daily Schedule. An aide assists the principal in meeting the demands of a work schedule, by facilitating the movement of the principal throughout the day. The aide should therefore always be familiar with the principal's daily schedule and the itinerary as it relates to meetings and event participation.

Where applicable for meetings/events, final preparations should be made the prior day by verifying the location, start time, entrance arrangement, staging and/or seating arrangements, and coordinating with other notable participants. The aide may accompany the principal to the meeting/event, and should have arranged for the Point of Contact to be available upon arrival to confirm arrangements and provide direction. Ensure that there is sufficient time for, and know the location of restrooms, and carry a light snack and bottled water. If driving a car for the principal, it is useful to map the route and determine travel time on the prior day.

The ADC should learn the principal's preference with respect to time availability beyond the meeting or event, so that the aide can ensure the principal stays on schedule. It is the aide's responsibility to alert the principal about time constraints and be ready to move that person, when time is of the essence. The aide should always maintain a low profile at meetings/events, staying at a distance from the principal, but remaining near enough to provide support when needed.

Protocol. The aide should always adhere to proper uniformed service protocol and military courtesy in the presence of the principal, to include the following: walk about one-half pace behind and to the left of the principal; unless holding the door open, allow the principal to pass through a doorway first; allow the principal to enter and exit an elevator first; open and close the rear right door of an automobile for the principal; if the aide is not driving, he should enter first in order to sit in the back seat to the principal's left side.

The aide may be tasked with calling "Attention on Deck!" just prior to the principal entering a room that is occupied primarily by uniformed service members. Only execute the call when the principal is the ranking officer.

Travel. The aide may have significant responsibilities that relate to official travel by the principal. Travel preparations – developing the itinerary, making contacts with the Point of Contact for the host organization, and numerous other tasks need to be accomplished with skill and competency. Upon return, the aide may be charged with preparing reimbursement vouchers, trip reports and thank you notes, as appropriate. See the Section, *Escort Officer,* below, for detailed information regarding the aide's responsibilities when accompanying the principal on official business that involves travel.

Uniform Inspection. The aide will be responsible for inspecting the principal's uniform prior to an event to ensure that it is squared away, checking for such items as cleanliness, inclusion of all components, and proper alignment of devices and ribbons. Any adjustments to the principal's uniform should be handled in private. It is advised that the ADC maintain extra accoutrements and other uniform supplies in the event the principal may lack an item.

Escort Officer

An escort officer refers to the officer who is temporarily assigned to a flag officer or dignitary ("the principal"), to meet and accompany the principal (also referred to as a distinguished visitor or DV) who is arriving from out-of-town. Absent a principal's regular aide-de-camp, the escort will serve as the aide-de-camp and brief the principal and guide that person in accordance with the official itinerary. The aide-de-camp (see the Section, *Aide-de-Camp,* above) and escort officer perform duties that are quite similar when the principal is on official business. An escort officer typically does not wear an aide's aiguillette; however, in the PHS, escort officers may be accorded this custom in recognition of their responsibility and to make others aware that an official duty is being performed. In both roles – aide-de-camp and escort officer – PHS officers are called upon to provide information and assistance in support of the principal.

Personal Qualities

Like an aide-de-camp, the escort officer must have an exemplary uniformed service appearance and bearing. He/she should be familiar with uniformed service customs, courtesy, protocol and social etiquette. He must be self-reliant, resourceful, and able to organize and carry out a myriad of tasks competently and with good judgment. His grooming and uniforms are maintained in accordance with the highest standards.

Distinguished Visitor

A distinguished visitor may be a high-ranking PHS officer such as the Surgeon General, a civilian official of the Department of Health and Human Services, or any individual or group identified in the Department of Defense *Table of Precedence*. A visit by a DV is an important event and it is essential that thorough planning and preparation be accomplished for the visit to be a success.

Escort Basics

The DV travels to conduct official business, and it is important that the logistical side of the visit be accomplished efficiently and competently. The escort should keep the following in mind.

- Always be well groomed, and wear a clean and pressed uniform.
- Always be on time and earlier if possible.
- Always practice uniformed service courtesy and adhere to official protocol.
- Always act professionally and maintain a formal uniformed service bearing while in public view.
- Always remember to subordinate your desires to the needs of the DV.

Notification

Upon receiving notification, the local escort officer (hereinafter referred to as "escort") will ensure that information pertaining to the visit is received well in advance. The escort should call the DV's office and, if the DV is the Surgeon General or Deputy Surgeon General, also call the aide. The escort should introduce himself/herself, request information about the visit and provide contact information. Pertinent information includes the following.

- Purpose and dates of visit.
- Names, titles and duties of all persons in the official party, including a picture(s) if possible.
- Itinerary, including a detailed schedule of daily activities and locations.
- Travel information, including mode of transportation, arrival and departure times, and ground transportation requirements.
- Accommodations information, including existing or needed reservations.
- Special needs or requests, such as dietary restrictions, entertainment, rest periods.
- When the DV's spouse is also traveling, information about the spouse's participation and need for social activities during the DV's official visit.

Pre-Arrival Preparations

The escort will ensure that the following arrangements have been made prior to arrival of the DV.

Arrival and Ground Transportation

- Ensure that a full sized vehicle (if available) is reserved and the driver, whether the escort or another person, knows the directions and actual route to the DV's destinations.
- Unless waived by the DV, arrange for a senior officer/official to be present at the arrival and departure of a flag rank or equivalent civilian official.

Accommodations

- Ensure that lodging is appropriate and reserved.
- If the DV has an aide or escort traveling with him/her, ensure that their quarters are in keeping with their standing as part of the official party.

Event Site and Itinerary

- Visit the location of event sites with the local coordinator in advance to learn details about the following: where the official car will stop and where it will be parked; who will greet the DV; the location of the facility entrance/exit; and, seating and stage arrangement. Review the written introduction and schedule of activities for the DV, and include an appropriate amount of time for the DV to personally greet people. Ensure that all arrangements conform to official protocol. Prepare written notes that can be given to the DV.
- Ensure that the itinerary provides sufficient time for occasional rest periods, coffee breaks, meals, change of clothes, and transportation. Review menu items to ensure they conform to any dietary restrictions.
- Confirm the dress requirement for all scheduled activities.
- Know about the availability of local dry cleaners, pharmacies, and emergency medical care.

Verification

- Call the DV's office and aide with any revisions to the itinerary and other information that may impact the DV's visit. If an event program is available, send it to the DV before the visit commences. Once verified, prepare other local officers to be on station ready status should they be needed.

DV's Arrival

The escort should follow certain steps to ensure a smooth DV pick-up.

Arrive Early

- Be present at the airport terminal or train depot arrival point about 30 minutes before the DV's scheduled arrival time. If practicable, and consistent with terminal security, position the car near the arrival point.
- Confirm the arrival time on visual displays inside the terminal and stand at the arrival gate to wait for the DV.

Meet DV

- Greet and introduce yourself to the DV – "Good morning (*afternoon, evening*), Admiral. I am (*rank, first and last name*) and I will be your escort officer during your visit."
- Assist with the DV's luggage.
- Open and close the car's right rear door for the DV, who will sit on the right side of the back seat. If not driving, the escort either enters the right rear door first to sit in the back seat to the DV's left side; or, enters through the left rear door, safety permitting.
- Give a brief description of the day's itinerary. Provide the DV with a folio that includes the program, itinerary, notes, names of event principals, a small map of the area, and your contact information.
- Carry all materials (e.g., brief case) for the DV throughout the visit.

From this moment forward, the escort is on duty until released by the DV.

Itinerary

If stopping at the hotel first, assist with the luggage and accompany the DV to the hotel registration area. Once registered, agree on a time to meet in the lobby to proceed to the next destination or event. Inspect the DV's uniform in a private area before proceeding with the itinerary.

Plan to arrive at the scheduled event about 30 minutes beforehand and, upon arrival, escort the DV to the DV greeter. When walking with the DV, stay to that person's left and about one-half pace behind. When approaching a door, the escort moves forward to hold the door open.

The escort will either assist the DV during the event or, if not directly involved, remain in the proximity of the DV. Keep easy eye contact with the DV and be prepared to assist, as needed.

The aide, escort or protocol officer may be responsible for numerous other tasks associated with a DV visit. PHS officers should consult protocol guidance documents for further information.

Planning

For those officers serving as an aide/escort to a DV, a planning checklist is provided in Appendix D.

Service Boards

The USPHS administers several boards that provide program support for the OSG and Division of Commissioned Corps Personnel and Readiness (DCCPR). PHS officers who meet specified criteria may volunteer to serve on a board, which provides a meaningful experience for the officer and an important service to the Corps. Among the more prominent boards are the following.

Appointment Board (AB)
The Appointment Board assesses the fitness and qualifications of candidates for appointment to the Regular and Reserve Corps. The Board determines whether or not a candidate is professionally qualified for appointment to the Corps. The Surgeon General or his/her designee makes the final decision with respect to the Board's recommendation. ABs are comprised of three or more active duty officers who serve for a period of one year. The majority of Board members are of the same professional category as the candidates for which the Board is convened. To be considered for this Board, an officer must be in the Regular Corps, be at a senior grade (o-5) and above, and have at least five years of Commissioned Corps active duty experience. The senior officer of the Board is designated as the Chairperson, and the Director, DCCPR shall assign a non-voting executive secretary.

Medical Review Board (MRB)
The Medical Review Board reviews and makes formal recommendations regarding an officer's medical fitness for duty and performance capability. To be eligible for disability retirement or separation, an officer must be found unable to perform the duties of his/her grade, category, or office because of physical or mental conditions of a permanent nature. If an officer is eligible for disability benefits, the MRB determines the rating for each compensable disability. The MRB is comprised of three or more senior officers in the medical category who are board eligible or certified in a clinical specialty, or qualified by experience; a senior dental officer may also be appointed as a member. The majority of the members considering psychiatric cases shall be board eligible or certified in psychiatry. The Chief, Medical Branch, shall serve as the Board's executive secretary. An officer may appeal the findings and recommendations of the MRB to the Medical Appeals Board, which is comprised of three or more PHS medical officers, one of whom shall be designated to serve as president of the Board.

Promotion Boards
The Annual Temporary Promotion Board (ATPB) and Annual Permanent Promotion Board (APPB) assess the qualifications, capabilities and performances of PHS officers eligible for promotion to the next higher temporary or permanent grade, respectively. The ATPBs/APPBs make their evaluation

based upon certain precepts and category-specific benchmarks. The precepts include at least the following factors: performance rating and reviewing official statement; education, training, and professional development; career progress and potential; professional contributions and service to the Corps; and, force readiness. For each temporary grade, an officer who is not otherwise eligible for review in the current promotion year may be considered one time by an ATPB for an Exceptional Proficiency Promotion.

One or more ATPBs/APPBs are constituted at least once each calendar year for each professional category. ATPBs/APPBs are comprised of three or more officers at the rank/grade of Captain (o-6). Insofar as it is practicable, the majority of Board members shall be Regular Corps officers in the same professional category as the officers being examined for promotion. The senior officer of the Board serves as the Chairperson. No officer may serve as an ATPB/APPB member for the same category more frequently than once every three years. An effort is made to ensure that the ATPB/APPB membership is representative with respect to agency/OpDiv and field representation.

Service on these and other boards require that Board members maintain in strict confidence all information with respect to individual officers and the deliberations of the Boards.

Chief Professional Officer

There are eleven professional categories within the Commissioned Corps: dental, dietitian, engineer, environmental health, health services (includes allied clinical care providers, computer science, health information management, hospital administration, public health education), medical, nurse, pharmacist, scientist, therapist, and veterinarian. Each of these categories is represented by a Chief Professional Officer (CPO). The CPO provides leadership, direction and coordination of their professional category, and serves as an advocate for the category in areas of interest to the Corps. The CPO is the liaison between the professional category and the Office of the Surgeon General, and he/she offers guidance and advice to the Surgeon General and administrative committees on matters such as recruitment, retention and career development of officers within their profession.

The selection of a Chief Professional Officer in the dental, engineer, nurse, and pharmacist categories is required by statute, and includes promotion of the nominee to a temporary flag grade for the duration of service as a CPO, after which they revert to their highest temporary grade if they remain on active duty. The Surgeon General may also appoint a CPO for other professional categories when it would benefit the USPHS; however, there is no requirement for promotion of these nominees to a flag grade. It has been customary for the SG to appoint a CPO for all professional categories.

Eligibility

Source: Instruction CC23.4.6, 13 February 2008.

To be considered for the position of a CPO, an officer must meet certain minimum nomination criteria. These include the following.

- Be appointed in, and hold his Corps commission as a member of the professional category for which the CPO is to be selected.
- Be a member of the Regular Corps and hold either the temporary or permanent pay grade of 0-6.
- Have served at least 12 years of active duty with the uniformed services. At least six active duty years must be as a USPHS officer.
- Have no more than 30 years of service creditable for purposes of determining eligibility to retire.
- Maintain current professional licensure when required, and meet any additional category-specific criteria.

Because the CPO appointment is in addition to the officer's responsibilities in his permanent duty assignment, a prospective nominee's agency must agree to the nominee serving up to a four year term and including, if applicable, beyond completion of 30 years of active service.

Personal and Professional Qualities

The CPO should be a person of integrity, with demonstrated leadership and management abilities. The CPO will serve as a distinguished role model to all officers in the CPO's professional category, so the prospective candidate needs to be highly regarded among his peers and others with whom that person is known. A CPO Nomination Board is convened for each professional category to review the professional credentials of candidates. Principal factors used to evaluate CPO candidates include the following.

- Annual performance ratings and evaluations on the Commissioned Officers' Effectiveness Reports.
- Past assignments, licensure status, force readiness and education.
- Awards received from the Corps and other uniformed services.
- Special professional qualifications, such as board certification and other specific credentials.
- Scope and variety of Corps assignments and responsibilities over the course of the individual's career.
- Recommendations from current and past agency heads and senior officials, the officers' vision statements and other pertinent documents.

Following its review of all eligible candidates, the CPO Nomination Board will select no more than five officers and rates them as either qualified or highly qualified, with any special justification. The Board's recommendations are forwarded to the Surgeon General for final decision.

Honor Cadre

The USPHS Honor Cadre, formed in 1999 by the Surgeon General, is known as "The Surgeon General's Own." The Honor Cadre functions in the capacity of a military color guard, which derives from a time when flags were carried into battle as an identifying symbol and rallying point for troops. Today, that practice has been superseded by color guards that carry the colors (national and organizational flags) at uniformed service and civil ceremonies and events.

Mission
The Honor Cadre represents the Commissioned Corps and the Office of the Surgeon General at formal and informal HHS and non-HHS sponsored events. In so doing, the Honor Cadre provides a valuable service to HHS, enhances visibility of the USPHS Commissioned Corps among HHS and non-HHS programs and organizations, and engenders esprit de corps.

Ceremonial Unit
The Ceremonial Unit presents the colors at ceremonies and events sponsored by the OSG, agencies and operating divisions of HHS, and appropriate non-HHS events. Awards ceremonies, promotion and retirement ceremonies, memorial services, and special events are among the types of venues served.

Basic Standards
The Honor Cadre is composed of officers who have shown exceptional commitment to, and pride in the PHS Commissioned Corps. Honor Cadre members must meet exceptionally high standards of professionalism to be selected for this special duty. To be considered, prospective members must be in excellent physical condition and meet certain height and weight standards and, without exception, have an exemplary military appearance and bearing.

Officers are considered probationary members for the initial six month period of service in the Honor Cadre. Inspection knowledge and precision drill are essential and this is accomplished through regularly scheduled practices. Officers should be thoroughly familiar with uniformed service courtesies and protocol. Uniforms are worn daily with pride and distinction. Regular or permanent membership is granted when: all uniforms deemed necessary for full participation are acquired; the officer attains drill and ceremony proficiency; attendance at practice and assigned ceremonial duties meets prescribed standards; and the officer shows the ongoing positive attitude of an exemplary officer.

Color Guard
The U.S. flag is known as the national color or color *(singular)* and, when it is carried with organizational flags by color-bearing units, the flags together are referred to as colors. It is considered an honor for uniformed service personnel to carry the colors.

Composition

A color guard unit is most often comprised of four individuals: two color bearers in the center and one color guard on each side of the color bearers. Whereas in the armed forces each guard carries a rifle, in the USPHS each guard carries a PHS sword. The national color is given the honor position on the marching right, with organizational and positional flags to the left. The senior officer in the color guard commands the unit.

Color Guard Formation

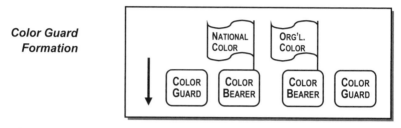

March

The color guard is formed and marched in one rank at close interval. The color guard marches at right shoulder arms, and wheels to the right or left to complete facing movements – these are executed with the command "Right (Left) Color Turn, March." To complete a wheeling movement, the guard nearest the direction of turn serves as the pivot point by marching in place while turning in the new direction. The other members shorten their steps and turn together in an arc, keeping abreast of each other to maintain forward alignment. When the new direction is reached, each member marches in place until the command "Halt" or "Forward, March" is given.

Salutes

In the military, when passing in review, the senior officer commands "Eyes, Right" at the prescribed saluting distance and the organizational color salutes (dips), and resumes the carry at the command "Ready, Front." Note that the guard on the right flank does not execute Eyes Right, and that the national color renders no salute. The organizational color salutes in all military ceremonies while the national anthem, "To the Color," or a foreign national anthem is played, and when rendering honors to the organizational commander (e.g., Surgeon General in the PHS), his/her direct representative, or an officer of equivalent or higher grade.

Presentation of the Colors

Posting and retiring the colors refers to displaying the colors, placing the colors in flag stands, and taking away the colors. The following procedures are used for posting and retiring the colors indoors. In PHS ceremonies, the colors may be marched to the front of the room and placed in flag stands, or they may be retired immediately after the playing of the national anthem.

The Honor Cadre may form outside or just inside the entrance to the auditorium, dining or meeting room. The audience is then directed to stand for the colors and national anthem. The Honor Cadre enters in a line formation, preferably, or in a column, and marches to the front center of the room or to the flag stands, and then turns to face the audience or other appropriate direction. The unit's commanding officer commands "Guard, Halt," and, "Present, Arms." The national anthem is played and, at its conclusion, the command is given to "Order, Arms." At this point, the Honor Cadre marches from the room with the colors (unless colors are posted).

The figures below show basic positions and movements associated with the sword when presenting the colors.

Figures 1. and 2. Military – Position of attention and Draw sword, respectively.

Figure 3. USPHS – Position of attention [Military – Carry sword]. The sword is held in the right hand, sword point up, with the wrist positioned just above the pelvic bone, and with the blade resting inside the right shoulder.

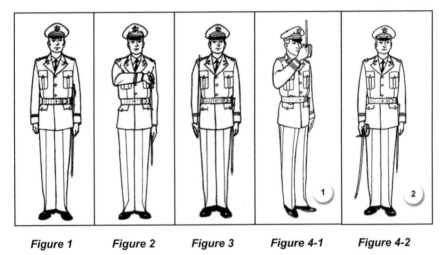

| Figure 1 | Figure 2 | Figure 3 | Figure 4-1 | Figure 4-2 |

Source: U.S. Army Field Manual 3-21.5

Figure 4-1. Present sword. On the command "Present, Arms" the sword is brought with the right hand to an upward, centered position, hilt at the chin, with the flat of the blade about four inches from the nose and facing outward at a 45 degree angle, and the blade facing level to the left.

Figure 4-2. To complete the movement, move the wrist and extend the arm so that the sword is outstretched at a 45-degree angle to the right, the blade facing down, the thumb extended on the left side of the grip, and the tip of the sword about 6 inches from the ground. On the command "Order, Arms" the sword is returned to the position of attention.

Junior Officer Advisory Group

The Junior Officer Advisory Group (JOAG) was chartered on December 7, 2001. It provides advice and consultation on interests and concerns specific to junior officers in the Commissioned Corps. Membership is for active duty officers with the rank of LCDR/o-4 and below, and an effort is made to have broad representation from among all PHS agencies staffed by junior officers. Junior officers are encouraged to actively participate in activities of the JOAG, because it is a great way to build fellowship and become more involved in the Commissioned Corps.

Mission
The Junior Officer Advisory Group provides advice and consultation to the Surgeon General, Professional Advisory Committees (PACs), Chief Professional Officers (CPOs), the Commissioned Officers Association and other Commissioned Corps groups on issues relating to professional practice and personnel activities that affect junior officers.

Objectives/Functions
The JOAG serves in a resource, advisory, and liaison capacity to assist in the development and coordination of activities related to junior officers in the Commissioned Corps with the following objectives.
- Identify and advocate on behalf of junior officers' issues and concerns.
- Assist the Office of the Surgeon General, Division of Commissioned Corps Personnel and Readiness, the Professional Advisory Committees and Chief Professional Officers in the assessment of personnel needs and recruitment, training, utilization, and recognition of junior officers.
- Develop position papers, statistical reports, and/or guidelines to advise and comment on issues relating to staffing and utilization, professional practice, and personnel activities affecting junior officers.
- Promote junior officer development and utilization.
- Promote cooperation and communication between junior and senior officers throughout the USPHS.
- Serve as a liaison between junior officers and other USPHS or external components.
- Serve as a communication link and informational resource for junior officers.

Membership

Composition and Term. Any USPHS junior officer who participates in the JOAG meetings and serves on a JOAG committee or workshop is considered an active participant of the JOAG. The JOAG is governed by voting members who serve in leadership positions. The JOAG has at least 11 and up to 20 voting members, comprised of one voting member endorsed by and representing each of the eleven PHS professional categories, and an additional nine at-large members. At least two members must have a duty station 75 miles or more away from the Washington, DC and Atlanta Metropolitan Areas. Efforts are made to ensure that the JOAG has broad representation from among all agencies, and does not consist entirely of one gender or race or ethnicity. Voting members serve a two year term, not to exceed a cumulative total of four years. Voting members are eligible to run for a position on the JOAG Executive Committee, including Chair, Vice-Chair, Chair-Elect, Executive Secretary, and Financial Liaison. And, there are eleven JOAG standing committees (e.g., Awards, Communications and Publications, Welcoming), each of which is chaired by a voting member of JOAG.

Nomination. Voting member terms are staggered so that approximately one-half of the members' terms expire annually. The JOAG operational year begins October 1. Each year, the JOAG Membership Committee will solicit nominations (including self-nominations) for upcoming vacancies. The names of respondents are sent to the nominees' respective CPO and agency head for elimination or endorsement. The Membership Committee will make member selections for new voting members, which are reviewed and approved by the JOAG. The names and nomination materials are then sent to the Surgeon General for concurrence and appointment.

Senior Advisor
A JOAG Senior Advisor will serve as a resource, advisor, and liaison to assist in the development and coordination of activities related to junior officers. The Advisor acts in a consultative capacity, advising on JOAG-related issues, concerns, policies, and procedures. He/she also serves as a liaison between JOAG and the OSG, and speaks and advocates on behalf of the JOAG, but does not officially represent the JOAG. The Senior Advisor must be an officer at the rank of CAPT/o-6 or above, and is appointed by the Surgeon General as an ex-officio JOAG member for a three year term.

Liaison, Commissioned Corps

The operating divisions and principal agencies of the Department of Health and Human Services each employ a commissioned officer or civilian who serves as the Commissioned Corps Liaison within their respective organization. The Liaisons are the principal program contact for administrative and operational Commissioned Corps matters, and they work closely with the Division of Commissioned Corps Personnel and Readiness. They also serve as the Corps personnel officer, processing personnel actions and providing authoritative information to commissioned officers assigned to their program.

Minority Officers Liaison Council

The Minority Officers Liaison Council (MOLC) provides advice and consultation on issues related to the professional practice and professional activities of minority Commissioned Corps personnel. Membership is for ethnic minority officers from PHS agencies and organizations staffed by commissioned personnel.

The MOLC is comprised of four distinct ethnic minority officer groups or committees, as follows:

- American Indian/Alaskan Native Commissioned Officers Advisory Committee [AIANCOAC]
- Asian Pacific American Officers Committee [APAOC]
- Black Commissioned Officers Advisory Group [BCOAG]
- Hispanic Officers Advisory Committee [HOAC]

The Council was originally formed in 1990 when Surgeon General Antonia Novello, the first woman and first Hispanic to be appointed to that post, recognized the need for a coalition of the minority groups to advise the SG.

Mission
Source: MOLC Charter, 11 January 2012.

The mission of the Minority Officers Liaison Council is to advise and serve the Office of the Surgeon General on issues of professional development and to advocate for the recognition of contributions made by minority officers in the U.S. Public Health Service.

Objectives

The purpose of the MOLC is to serve as the liaison between the Office of Surgeon General and the minority groups. The Council serves in a resource and advisory capacity to assist in the development, coordination, and evaluation of activities related to ethnic minority officers in all professional categories, with the specific objectives of:

- Advocating for and promoting professional development and career advancement of minority officers.
- Coordinating and facilitating communication among the four chartered minority advisory groups (CMAGs) and between the CMAGs, agencies, and operating divisions to which officers are assigned.
- Identifying minority officer and CMAG issues and providing advice to the OSG on these issues.
- Supporting the USPHS mission through recruitment, retention, and promotion of minority officers in leadership and management positions.
- Serving as a communication link and information resource between OSG and the CMAGs.

Membership

Composition. The Minority Officers Liaison Council membership consists of eight voting members, with two voting representatives from each of the four CMAGs. Efforts are made to have the broadest representation among voting members, to include the following: senior officers (five or more years in the USPHS) and junior officers; gender representation; individuals with diverse backgrounds; members from across assigned agencies and professional disciplines; and those whose duty station is 75 or more miles away from the Washington, DC Metropolitan Area. Voting members serve a term of one year. Non-voting members include the following: immediate past MOLC Chair and Junior Officer Advisory Group Representative serving one additional year as ex-officio members; policy/technical advisors serving as ad hoc members; and, a Senior Advisor at the rank of Captain or above to advise the MOLC and MOLC Chair.

MOLC Officers. To ensure that each CMAG has an equal voice in Council proceedings, there is a yearly rotation of the positions of responsibility. Council officers include the positions of Chair, Vice Chair, Secretary, and Liaison, who serve a one year term on a rotational schedule.

Music Ensemble

The USPHS Commissioned Corps Music Ensemble is the official PHS musician group at ceremonial and other occasions. It was originally formed in July 2000 under the sponsorship of the Scientist Professional Advisory Committee. Known as "The Surgeon General's Own," the Music Ensemble has since become a well-recognized presence at about 25 events each year.

Mission

The USPHS Music Ensemble represents the Office of the Surgeon General and provides musical support for formal and informal HHS and appropriate non-HHS sponsored events. In so doing, the Ensemble provides a valuable service to HHS, enhances visibility of the USPHS Commissioned Corps among programs and organizations, and engenders esprit de corps.

Performance Venues

The Ensemble performs at ceremonies and events sponsored by HHS and other agencies and organizations. Events include award, promotion and retirement ceremonies; official receptions; professional meetings; special events; and, funeral/memorial services. Notably, the Ensemble has performed at every annual Scientific and Training Symposium since 2000 and, in recent years, at the National World War II Memorial and the Smithsonian National Air and Space Museum on the National Mall in Washington, DC.

Composition

The USPHS Music Ensemble is comprised of three groups:

* Choral Group
* Ceremonial Band (Instrumental)

The main Music Ensemble groups are located in the Washington, DC Metropolitan Area. Other groups, field officers and support personnel are located throughout the U.S. Organized groups currently operate in the following areas: DC Metropolitan Area; Atlanta, GA; Butner, NC; and Dallas, TX. Each group is capable of performing independently or in concert with one another and is directed by a PHS officer serving as the Group Leader.

Unlike U.S. Military Bands where appointment to a Musician billet is the principal duty assignment, those officers who comprise the Music Ensemble participate in this activity in addition to their regularly assigned duties. Ensemble membership therefore calls for a particular dedication to the Corps, yet it can be a highly rewarding experience for those who accept the challenge.

Standards

Any active duty or retired PHS officer in good standing is eligible to become a member of the Music Ensemble. Prospective members should already have an acceptable level of music training and/or experience.

Officers are considered probationary members for the first six months of service in the Ensemble, after which they are eligible for full membership and a letter of appointment from the Surgeon General. Full membership is granted when: the officer attains an acceptable level of musical proficiency; the officer meets prescribed standards for attendance at rehearsals, practices and performances; and, the officer shows ongoing commitment to mission.

Members of the Ensemble volunteer their personal time and talent, to include a sometimes demanding schedule of rehearsals that are normally held during non-duty hours. Ensemble performances at official events are often held during duty hours, so supervisory support for the member is required. Because they represent the Office of the Surgeon General, Ensemble members are expected to conduct themselves in a highly professional manner, maintain their uniforms in excellent condition, and to be thoroughly familiar with uniformed service protocol and performance etiquette.

Oversight

The Office of the Surgeon General oversees the Music Ensemble in consultation with an Executive Director (or two Co-Executive Directors), who is appointed by the Surgeon General as administrator and is responsible for all operational aspects of the Ensemble. The Executive Director, an Executive Assistant and the Group Leaders, who are responsible for music selection, rehearsal and performance arrangements, form the Music Ensemble Executive Committee which provides ongoing supervision of the Music Ensemble.

Professional Advisory Committee

Each of the eleven USPHS professional categories has a Professional Advisory Committee (PAC). The Professional Advisory Committee provides advice on professional and personnel matters to its Chief Professional Officer (CPO) and the Surgeon General. Membership is representative of employees of the PHS and other Federal agencies where officers are assigned. Membership on a PAC offers commissioned officers and civilian employees the opportunity to learn about and become involved with colleagues in the issues and policies that affect their profession. Because work is largely accomplished through subcommittees, officers can become involved as a subcommittee or working group member, which does not require formal membership on the PAC.

Mission
The Professional Advisory Committee provides advice and consultation to the Surgeon General on issues relating to the professional practice and personnel activities of those in the respective professional category, who are Civil Service employees (CS) or PHS Commissioned Corps officers. The PAC provides similar advisory assistance to the Chief Professional Officer and, upon request, to the agency and/or program heads of the Public Health Service and non-PHS agencies that employ PHS personnel.

Objectives
The PAC serves in a resource and advisory capacity to assist in the development, coordination and evaluation of PHS professional activities, with the specific objectives of:

- Identifying and facilitating the resolution of issues of concern as they relate to the professional category/discipline.
- Assessing professional personnel needs and assisting in meeting those needs through activities in recruitment, training, utilization, and recognition of professional category/discipline members.
- Developing position papers, statistical reports, and/or guidelines where appropriate, in order to advise and comment on matters relating to both personnel and professional practice issues.
- Promoting the development and utilization of the subject professionals by the PHS and other governmental programs.
- Promoting cooperation and communication among the subject professionals and other health professionals.
- Promoting all aspects of the professional category/discipline throughout the agencies/operating divisions and programs of the PHS.
- Providing liaison to professional disciplines within and among PHS components, and providing advice and consultation to the agency heads and operating programs upon request.

Relation to Organizations

In carrying out its responsibilities, the PAC operates in an advisory capacity. It does not substitute for line management or in any way exercise the prerogatives of the respective operating programs. Members are representative of PHS agencies/operating divisions of HHS and non-HHS agencies and, while members are chosen from the respective organizations, they neither represent agency management nor speak for the agency. Members are knowledgeable professionals who represent a cross section of the interests, concerns and responsibilities of their colleagues in the organizations staffed by PHS personnel.

PAC Designations

The Professional Advisory Committees correspond with each of the eleven USPHS professional categories and include the following:

Dental Professional Advisory Committee (DePAC)

Dietitian Professional Advisory Committee (D-PAC)

Engineer Professional Advisory Committee (EPAC)

Environmental Health Officer Professional Advisory Committee (EHOPAC)

Health Services Professional Advisory Committee* (HS PAC)
*Includes over 50 professional disciplines, with nine Professional Advisory Groups (PAGs) that address discipline-specific issues.

Nursing Professional Advisory Committee (N-PAC)

Pharmacist Professional Advisory Committee (PharmPAC)

Physician Professional Advisory Committee (PPAC)

Scientist Professional Advisory Committee** (SciPAC)
**Includes over 40 scientific disciplines.

Therapist Professional Advisory Committee (TPAC)

Veterinarian Professional Advisory Committee (VetPAC)

Membership

Composition and Term. The Professional Advisory Committee is comprised of both civilian and commissioned officer members within the particular professional category. The PAC may have from 7 to 20 voting members, who serve a term of three years, not to exceed a cumulative total of six years. Efforts are made to have the broadest representation possible with regard to the following: there are members from among all agencies staffed by commissioned officers; the PAC will not consist entirely of CS or Corps personnel; at least two members' duty station is 75 or more miles away from the Washington, DC Metropolitan Area; distributed gender and ethnicity/race representation; and, distributed professional seniority, with at least one member with fewer than five years and one member with at least eleven years of professional experience. The CPO serves as an ex-officio (non-voting) member; the former Chairperson may serve one additional year as an ex-officio member; and, liaison members may be appointed as ex-officio members of the PAC.

Nomination. Annually, the PAC will solicit, through broadcast e-mail and newsletters, nominations (including self-nominations) for vacancies on the PAC. The names of respondents are sent by the CPO to the nominees' respective agency head for endorsement. The PAC and CPO will then identify, by name, highly qualified individuals, and a final list of nominees is sent by the CPO to the Surgeon General for approval. Member terms are staggered so that approximately one-third of the members' terms expire annually.

Protocol Officer

A protocol officer is an officer or civilian who oversees the implementation of official protocol standards for an institution or organization. In the Federal government, the protocol officer provides fulltime management and support service to high ranking government officials, flag officers and to commands that are commanded by a senior officer (hereinafter referred to as the "commander"). The protocol officer advises the commander and staff on uniformed service customs and courtesies, tradition, organization and policy. Their responsibilities include detailed planning for visits by distinguished visitors (DVs), official travel, conferences, recognition programs, special ceremonies and official social functions. The protocol officer also maintains a protocol library for the command. A protocol officer serves as a representative of the commander or command to which assigned, and it is imperative that whatever actions are taken are consistent with established protocol and carried out as flawlessly as possible. The military employs hundreds of protocol officers who receive specialized training in order to ensure that all activities are conducted professionally and in accordance with government, military and social protocol. In the military, the position of protocol officer is one of the more sensitive and challenging positions in a command – the ability of the command to manage events and projects that have high visibility will reflect favorably, or unfavorably, upon the leadership.

Background and Knowledge
Those who serve as a protocol officer should have certain basic qualifications. It is essential that the protocol officer have a comprehensive understanding of his/her own service and familiarity with other uniformed services – their history, mission, organization, and general operating procedures. A PHS protocol officer needs to have knowledge about the agencies to which PHS officers are assigned and, over time, have an acquaintance with the principal officials of those agencies.

The protocol officer is an authority on government, uniformed service and social customs, traditions, courtesies and protocol. To learn this well, protocol officers receive formal training provided by the uniformed service or a protocol school outside the service, and are expected to maintain proficiency through self-directed study.

Personal Qualities

The protocol officer must have a strong sense of integrity in his dealings with others and be capable of making good decisions at all times. He/she must be prepared for any contingency and, if mistakes are made, the protocol officer must move ahead without making excuses. Through his actions, the protocol officer must attain a level of confidence by the commander. There are certain attributes, which follow, that a protocol officer needs in order to carry out the position duties with proficiency.

Communication Skills. The protocol officer must be skilled in both verbal and written communication. Much depends on the maintenance of good interpersonal communications, and the ability of the protocol officer to listen well and communicate clearly with others is critical. A protocol officer works directly with the commander, other command leadership and principal staff, so a good communications relationship needs to be formed between the officer and the leadership – he must be comfortable in discussing any matter with the leadership on a one-on-one basis.

Cooperation and Teamwork. The protocol officer needs to be a leader in attitude and action. He must be able to work effectively with all persons, and be a conciliator who is sensitive to the motivations and needs of others. It is important to instill a sense of cooperation and teamwork among those involved in an event or project, so the officer needs to be a person who can bring others together in a common purpose.

Organization and Resourcefulness. The protocol officer must be able to properly organize and prioritize the myriad of details that accompany his duties in planning a complex event. The ability to gather, review and disseminate information in an orderly way is critical to accomplishing the mission.

The effective protocol officer is also resourceful. He will have sufficient knowledge and experience to plan in advance for, and meet any contingency with competence. While most events or projects will require coordinated teamwork, a protocol officer must be ready to personally take whatever action is necessary to complete a project, even if such tasks might ordinarily be performed by others.

Appearance. The protocol officer must have an appearance that is in keeping with proper military appearance and bearing. The appearance of the protocol officer impacts significantly on the perception that others have of the commander and command. If a commissioned officer, one's uniforms are to be maintained in conformance with the highest uniform standards. Knowledge of the proper dress for different occasions is essential, both for himself and when he may be called upon to advise the leadership.

Readiness Force

Under the National Response Framework (2nd ed., 2013), HHS is the Primary Agency designated to provide personnel, materiel and logistical support to meet the needs of the Public Health and Medical Services Emergency Support Function (ESF #8). PHS commissioned officers are the principal response resource and their duties include preparing for and responding to urgent medical and public health emergencies, both nationally and internationally, in addition to performing their regular position responsibilities. The Readiness and Response Program (RRP) in the Division of Commissioned Corps Personnel and Readiness administers the activities related to training and deployment of officers. Formerly known as the PHS Commissioned Corps Readiness Force (CCRF) and, subsequently, the Office of Force Readiness and Deployment (OFRD), officers will see these two program acronyms still in use.

Mission
The program mission is to provide public health leadership and expertise in times of extraordinary need during disasters, strife, or other public health emergencies, in response to Federal, tribal, state, local or international requests. The PHS must be ready to respond to natural and intentional public health disasters. To that end, it is essential that PHS officers have the knowledge, training and preparation to quickly mobilize for any foreseeable type of disaster relief in the U.S. and abroad. Didactic and field training requirements, as well as maintenance of specified medical/physical standards and professional competencies, are prescribed for all officers. Training may include provision for building interoperability – the capability to operate in concert with other uniformed service personnel. Officers must therefore place a high premium on being personally and professionally prepared for any contingency.

Operations
Assistance Requests. Requests for Commissioned Corps assistance may be in response to any of the following:
- A national emergency as declared by the President;
- A public health emergency as declared by the President or Secretary;
- An urgent public health need: a critical staffing shortage of health care/-public health personnel within a facility or program administered by an OPDIV/STAFFDIV or non-HHS organization that threatens the health and safety of the affected population; or, a crisis response, a situation presenting a significant threat to the public health of a State, Tribe, or local community, and available resources are inadequate to respond; or
- A National Special Security Event declared by the Secretary of Homeland Security, is of national significance, requires special security, and is coordinated at the national response level.

Once the mission requirements are determined, RRP will match the requirement against the qualifications of officers on that month's rotational ready roster and, if necessary, deploy preconfigured rapid response teams that can be at the disaster site within a matter of hours.

Activation Process. The process for activating Commissioned Corps deployments is a stepwise procedure, summarized as follows.

- Request for Assistance – RRP evaluates the need and whether it will involve an appropriate utilization of commissioned officers.
- Request for Activation – RRP submits a formal request for activation to the Surgeon General, who briefs the Secretary and/or designee. If the Secretary/designee concurs, ready rosters of officers are activated.
- Identification of Assets – Needs of the mission are matched with the skills and qualifications of officers on the rotational ready roster, and individual officers are identified. In some instances, the requirements of the mission may exceed the capability of a single ready roster, and multiple rosters are utilized and/or rapid response teams may be activated.
- Deployment – Officers are contacted and their agencies are informed of the need, and supervisory release is obtained. If necessary, travel orders and arrangements are prepared, and teams/officers are deployed.

There are five rotational rosters, each of which has representation from all professional categories. Officers are on-call during the month that their roster is active. Officers must confirm their availability and the roster then represents the pool of officers that could respond during that time period.

Basic Standards
Source: PHS Manual Circular No. 377, 02 July 2004; PPM 04-003, 04 October 2004; PPM 07-001, 03 November 2006.

All commissioned officers are required to meet the Basic Level of Force Readiness. Standards for the Basic level are as follows.

- *Health and Safety Standards* – Disaster settings often require physical exertion, to include working 12+ hour days, lifting, unloading, and carrying equipment and supplies, and walking significant distances. Healthcare workers are also at risk for exposure to and possible transmission of infectious diseases. Officers therefore need to be involved with ongoing personal health maintenance and improvement. The process includes monitoring of officers' health and well-being through the following:
  - Medical History, Recordation of Height and Weight (annually).
  - Physical and Dental Examinations (every five years).
  - Immunizations – Influenza (annually); Tuberculin Skin Test (PPD); Hepatitis A, Hepatitis B, MMR (measles, mumps, rubella), Tetanus/-Diphtheria (TD), and Varicella (chickenpox) immunizations (per recommended schedule).

- *Physical Readiness Standards* – These standards ensure that the physical capabilities of officers are sufficient to meet their deployment roles. There are currently two physical fitness options for satisfying the physical readiness standards annually:
  - Meeting performance standards of the PHS Annual Physical Fitness Test (APFT), *or*
  - Completion of the President's Challenge Active Life Style Award (PALA) or the Presidential Champions Award Program.
- *Training Standards* – Officers must have proficiency in basic life support measures, and a basic understanding in the areas of public health and deployment-response activities. This is accomplished through:
  - Completing and maintaining currency in one of the following: American Heart Association Basic Life Support for Healthcare Providers, AHA Advanced Cardiac Life Support, or the American Red Cross CPR/AED for the Professional Rescuer.
  - Completion of twelve specified Web-based Readiness Training Modules for the Basic level of force readiness, as follows:

    HHS Responder e-Learn 2.0 Coursework:

110	Disaster Response	142	Disaster Triage
140	Preventive Medicine for Field Operations	180	Infectious Disease Management
141	Health Consequences and Response	182	Terrorism
		183	ABCs of Bioterrorism
		217	Safety and Security Awareness

    FEMA Emergency Management Institute Coursework:

IS-100	Introduction to Incident Command System
IS-200	ICS for Single Resources and Initial Action Incidents
IS-700a	National Incident Management System, An Introduction
IS-800b	National Response Framework, An Introduction

- *Professional Competency* – Officers must designate a Deployment Role. Those who are healthcare providers must have and maintain a current unrestricted professional license, certification or registration for his/her profession. Officers who want to deploy in a clinical role (dentist, EMT, medical technologist, mental health, nurse, nurse practitioner, optometrist, pharmacist, physician, physician assistant, therapist, veterinarian) must practice a minimum of 80 hours of direct patient care annually.
- *Uniforms* – Officers must have all required deployment uniforms.

Response Teams

The USPHS emergency response effort is comprised of a number of Teams that are organized by Tiers, corresponding with the urgency and type of emergency situation. The Tiers include Tier 1, Tier 2, Tier 3, and Tier 4, each of which is comprised of specified types of Teams that respond within set timeframes. The general structure of the PHS Tiered Response follows.

PHS Tiered Response Structure

TIER 1
11 - Regional Incident Support Teams (RIST)
[Deploy within 4-12 hours]

TIER 1
5 - National Incident Support Teams (NIST)
[Deploy within 12 hours]

TIER 1
5 - Rapid Deployment Force (RDF)
[Deploy within 12 hours]

TIER 2	TIER 2	TIER 2	TIER 2
5 – Applied Public Health Teams (APHT)	5 - Mental Health Teams (MHT)	5 – Services Access Teams (SAT)	5 – Capital Area Provider Teams (CAP)
[Deploy in 36 hrs.]	[Deploy in 36 hrs.]	[Deploy in 36 hrs.]	[Deploy in 36-72 hrs.]

TIER 3
5,000 Officers on-Call, Monthly Rotational Schedule
[Deploy within 72 hours]

TIER 4
Medical Reserve Corps, Ready Reserve

Deployment Preparation

PHS deployments can cover a range of geographic and situational conditions. Officers should always keep one suitcase packed with items that would be useful in any type of deployment. Some general things should be kept in mind.

- Luggage should be sturdy, and have a lock for use at the deployment site. Two pieces of luggage can be brought: one carry-on and one check-in bag. Do not pack more than you can carry. Keep at least one set of clothes, personal medications, and all professional equipment in the carry-on bag.
- Clothing and uniforms should be appropriate for the mission. Bring enough clothes and prescribed uniforms to last for 14 days, consistent with the weather, and include a light rain jacket. Boots should be broken in beforehand. Also, bring exercise clothes and comfortable shoes.
- Food for one day's worth of emergency need should be carried in the carry-on bag. Because TSA does not permit over 3 ounces of liquid to pass through security, bottled water should be purchased at the arrival airport for use at the deployment site. Possible food items may include items such as MREs (Meal, Ready-to-Eat), dehydrated food and cereal bars.
- Miscellaneous items to bring, in addition to personal care and toiletry items, include sun screen, sun glasses, insect repellent, sewing kit, shower shoes, small portable radio, reading materials, Zip Loc bags, and cash.

Surgeon General's Policy Advisory Council

The Surgeon General's Policy Advisory Council (SGPAC) constitutes a framework within which the Department of Health and Human Services (HHS) and other Federal agencies that utilize commissioned officers for providing advice to the Surgeon General (SG) and Deputy Surgeon General on policy matters related to the Commissioned Corps.

Objectives
The SGPAC is a resource and advisory group for the SG to evaluate policies affecting the Commissioned Corps, with the specific objectives of:
- Identifying policy issues that are of mutual concern to the Surgeon General and to the agencies.
- Advising the SG of potential impact on agencies of proposed Commissioned Corps policy and procedure issuances.
- Identifying and facilitating resolution of issues when conflicts of interest arise among different agencies.
- Serving as a forum for discussion of cross cutting issues that affect commissioned officers.

Membership and Authority
The SGPAC is comprised of a representative from each of the major HHS agencies/operating divisions and other non-HHS agencies to which PHS officers are assigned. SGPAC members are nominated by their respective agencies for a three-year term and approved by the Surgeon General. Members must be at the senior grade (o-5) or equivalent Civil Service grade, and above. The Deputy Surgeon General or designee serves as Chairperson of the SGPAC.

In carrying out its responsibilities, the SGPAC operates in an advisory capacity. The SGPAC members are the communication link between the SG, Office of the Surgeon General, and the agency Heads on policy issues pertaining to the Commissioned Corps. The SGPAC members speak on behalf of the agency they represent on specific policy issues related to the Corps. However, members do not substitute for line management or exercise the authorities of their respective operating programs, unless delegated by their programs.

CHAPTER SEVEN

COMMUNICATIONS

Virtually every aspect of professional and service life involves verbal and written communications. An officer's communication skills influence the perception of others about the officer. Effective interpersonal and organizational communications are also vital to the proper functioning of a group, and in promoting a positive corporate image of the uniformed service and organizational entity.

BUSINESS CARDS

CALLS & CARDS

CONVERSATION

CORRESPONDENCE

GREETINGS & INTRODUCTIONS

PRESENTATIONS & SPEAKING

TELECOMMUNICATIONS

Business Cards

Public Health Service commissioned officers should have a business/personal card, particularly if their position involves dealing with the public, or if they frequently attend large conferences and official meetings. The card provides an efficient means for providing contact information and is a way for others to remember you. Because of its importance and the fact that it represents you and the PHS, the business card should reflect quality in every respect.

Specifications
The form of business cards can vary widely, but a commissioned officer's card is conservative by design. The card conforms to the standard size of 3½ by 2 inches, allowing it to fit into a business card holder. If not already set by the command authority, the overall appearance, texture and color of card stock and print elements need to be carefully selected. Print characteristics include the color of print, font (typeface, size and style), and whether the card is printed, engraved, thermographed (raised print), embossed (the image is in relief, with or without ink), or some combination thereof.

Format

There are two standard business card formats used by uniformed service personnel, although the format may vary with respect to relative placement of information on the card. Unless specified, the officer's institutional logo (e.g., Department of Health and Human Services or agency to which assigned) is ordinarily located in the upper left corner of the card. Officers may also elect to use the USPHS Commissioned Corps logo alone or in concert with the institutional logo; if both are used, the logos are placed in upper opposing corners of the card. No more than two logos should be used. Standard formats that are customarily used by service personnel are as follows.

- An officer's name and academic degree and/or professional credentials are centered. Rank and uniformed service designation and position are placed on the next two lines or elsewhere on the card, as appropriate.

Sample 1
Business Card

 U.S. FOOD AND DRUG ADMINISTRATION

James E. Ford, PharmD
Captain, U.S. Public Health Service
Director, Division of Drug Information

CENTER FOR DRUG EVALUATION & RESEARCH
10903 NEW HAMPSHIRE AVENUE   TEL: (301) 555-1000
SILVER SPRING, MD 20993   EMAIL: fordj@fda.gov

- Some positions may require, or the officer may prefer, that rank appear on the first line preceding one's name. When using that format, there should be no post-nominals such as academic/professional credentials.

Sample 2
Business Card

 U.S. FOOD AND DRUG ADMINISTRATION

CAPT James E. Ford
U.S. Public Health Service
Director, Division of Drug Information

CENTER FOR DRUG EVALUATION & RESEARCH
10903 NEW HAMPSHIRE AVENUE   TEL: (301) 555-1000
SILVER SPRING, MD 20993   EMAIL: fordj@fda.gov

In addition to the duty station address and telephone number, business cards often include the facsimile number and e-mail address in a lower corner. Note that honorifics (e.g., Dr., Mr., Ms., etc.) are not used on business cards, in contrast to social cards. A nickname may be included only if well established (e.g., Admiral John ("Jack") Kearns).

Purpose
The business card is properly used as follows:
- To give professional and/or uniformed service identification information to another individual, such as a colleague, business contact, or patient.
- As a cover attachment to official documents being sent to others, to identify the sender.
- As an enclosure with a gift, to identify the sender if not well known to the recipient (although a gift card or calling card may be preferable).
- Occasionally, to serve as a medium for brief messages on the back.

Providing Card
Following are some guidelines for the use of business cards.
- Provide only crisp, clean, and up-to-date cards.
- Generally, provide your card to those who have shown an interest in receiving or exchanging such information. Reciprocate, when appropriate, when someone gives you their business card.
- Do not offer your card to officers who are superior in rank, unless there is evident interest in receiving your card.
- Business cards are usually exchanged at the beginning of a meeting, following introductions.
- Do not leave a pile of your cards or scatter them about at large general meetings or other such gatherings.
- Refrain from giving business cards at a strictly social event. However, if offered privately and not at the dinner table, it is generally alright.
- For close friends and those who are ill, a gift card or personal note is preferred as an enclosure with flowers or a gift.
- When used as an attachment or enclosure, you may write a note on the front or back (write "over" on the front) of the card. If the recipient is someone you know well, line out your printed name and sign your given (first) name.

Receiving Card
When someone gives you their business card, reciprocate with a business card of your own. Always take a moment to review their card and thank the person for giving you this information. This is particularly important in the international arena, where the business/name card and the protocol that surrounds it has considerable importance. It is improper to receive a business card and simply place it in your pocket or purse. If appropriate, a notation may be written on the back of the card about the person or any special information and follow-up actions to be taken.

Calls & Cards

Although PHS officers do not typically make official and social calls, it is important to have some familiarity with these military customs.

Official Calls

Upon arrival at a new duty station, a military officer officially reports for duty to the commanding officer (CO). Unless dispensed with by the senior officer, a courtesy call is also made by the officer on the CO in his/her office. These calls last about 10 to 15 minutes and afford the CO and officer an opportunity to learn about each other in a less formal meeting. Alternatively, at large stations where many officers are posted and time constraints preclude a personal meeting, an arriving officer may be introduced to the CO at the first officer staff meeting. The new officer may follow-up with a brief courtesy call.

Social Calls

Within two weeks of reporting for duty, social calls are made by an arriving officer and his/her spouse at the commanding officer's home, who in turn may return the call at the new officer's home. The new officer should limit the visit to 15 to 30 minutes unless requested to stay longer and, if expected, leave a calling/personal card upon departure. Though no longer common, these at-home visits are still the custom at some military stations in Europe.

More commonly today, the CO and his spouse periodically host receptions, occasionally at their residence, where hospitality is extended to officers of the command and their spouses. These functions are usually considered "calls made and paid," meaning that those in attendance need not reciprocate with an invitation to the CO and spouse. At large gatherings, attendees may be announced to the CO and his spouse, who greet each guest. When departing, officers should thank the host and hostess or send a short thank you note.

Calling and Attaché Cards

Calling cards are used for social calls and for making official calls in a foreign country. The uniformed service calling/personal card conforms to the standard size of 3½ by 2 inches. The officer's rank (spelled out), first name, middle initial and surname are placed in the center of the card, followed by the service designation in the lower right corner (no logo). Calling cards are conservative in design, with white or ecru card stock and black lettering.

When assigned to a foreign country, an officer is advised to contact the protocol officer of the American Embassy for guidance on the policy regarding official calls. Calling or attaché cards should be prepared in advance of the change in duty station. There is a prescribed format for attaché cards, and officers may either print both sides of the card, one side in English and the other in the language of the country to which assigned, or print two sets of cards, with English on one set and the other language on the second set.

Conversation

"There can be no doubt that of all the accomplishments prized in modern society, that of being agreeable in conversation is the very first. ...It is agreed among us that people must meet frequently, both men and women, and that not only is it agreeable to talk, but that it is a matter of common courtesy to say something, even when there is hardly anything to say."

From the Introduction to *The Principles of the Art of Conversation*, by J.P. Mahaffy, 1891.

Effective communication in business, the professions and uniformed services is essential to success. Most communication is verbal, involving the art of speaking and listening. Those officers who use good grammar and are best able to articulate their thoughts will be more successful in interacting with others. Although words are the primary medium, good body language is also a significant aspect of effective communication.

There are two principal types of verbal communication – official and social. In work situations, conversation may be more technical and to the point, yet under normal circumstances is pleasant with due deference to rank or seniority. Rank has its privileges and, when very senior personnel are present, the general rule is to allow senior officers to lead. This should not stifle candid discussions of a business nature by more junior staff.

Social settings provide an opportunity to engage in "small talk," which is also pleasant, but which has less import. Social conversation breaks down certain barriers and provides latitude with regard to the range of topics that can be discussed, as long as such discussions are cordial, generally involve non-controversial topics, and are not injurious to others or yourself.

Uniformed service officers customarily adhere to a certain protocol with regard to their verbal discourse with other officers.

- For conveying greetings from senior officers, use the form "Admiral Williams presents his compliments to Commander Jung and says..." (a junior officer does not "present his compliments" to a senior). For making an official or social call upon a senior officer, a junior officer correctly says "Admiral Williams, I came to pay my respects" or "Inform the Admiral that Commander Jung would like to pay his respects."
- In speaking with junior officers, senior officers who "direct," "desire," or "suggest" that something be done are, in effect, giving a directive or order. Junior officers should only "recommend" an action or "request" senior officers to act.
- Senior officers "call" or "direct attention" to something, whereas junior officers "invite attention."
- Senior officers acknowledge information provided by junior officers by responding "very well," whereas junior officers acknowledge a direct order with "yes, Sir."

Effective Speaking and Listening

Words can have many meanings, but if they are properly communicated and received, mutual understanding will occur. Other factors enter into verbal communication, however, and include the pitch, tone, volume and inflection of your voice; nonverbal forms of communication such as body language; and, the perception which the listener places on the message. In other words, how you say (and when listening, how you interpret) the spoken word can be as important as what is actually stated. Persons who are cognizant of these factors tend to be more adept in their official and social dealings. Those who also have a good conversational style have an added advantage – they can move through subjects with greater ease, making themselves more interesting and therefore more closely listened to by others.

The effectiveness in conveying your thoughts can depend, to a large extent, on the speaking tools that you employ and conversational etiquette you show toward others. For instance:

- Articulate words with an agreeable pitch, tonal quality, tempo or rate of speech, and volume of sound. Give expression to the words through appropriate variations in those vocal characteristics, so that real interest in the subject is evident to the listener. Avoid contrived speech characteristics. This does not preclude the need to modify one's normal speech pattern in appropriate circumstances; for example, a military leader who is trying to rally support for a mission will modify his/her delivery in a way that commands attention and gains acceptance of the message.

- Use proper grammar and a good working vocabulary that is conversational, natural and suited to your style. Avoid the following: filler words such as "uh" or "you know;" slang or words that are of passing fashion such as "you guys" (particularly when addressing men *and* women); technical jargon; profanity; prejudicial ethnic or religious terms; and words that are considered sexist.

- Think before you speak. Do not place another person in an uneasy position by what you say. Be mindful of the timing and appropriateness of subject matter, in terms of both the context of the conversation and who you are speaking with.

- Be alert to signs of boredom in listeners and adjust accordingly. Do not dominate a conversation.

- Do not interrupt others who are speaking, particularly those who are senior in rank, with corrections of their grammar, injection of words or phrases the speaker is searching for (unless it is apparent that the person needs assistance), or with the finish to a speaker's story.

- Show interest in speaking and listening through good body language. Greet others with a firm handshake. Stand or sit with posture comfortably erect. Give complete attention to those with whom you are conversing –

maintain good eye contact, avoid the "glazed" eye look or allowing your eyes to wander.

- Maintain good listening habits through concentration on the *thought* being conveyed. Take account of the speaker's choice of words and gestures used in conveying the thought. When a deficient speaker or an uninteresting subject places impediments to effective listening, the effective listener overcomes those barriers by recognizing his responsibility to be attentive to the speaker and what could be potentially important information. A method of enhancing one's interest and displaying it to the speaker is to make listening responses such as asking questions and nodding affirmatively. A note of caution regarding the latter behavior, however – leaders are not appreciative of junior officers who try to garner favor simply by appearing always to be in agreement with the senior officer.

Correspondence

The impression that others have of you as an individual and the uniformed service you represent will be made by both the form and content of your written communications. While e-mail is often employed in place of structured styles of written communication, it is important to forego the ease of an e-mail when a more formal approach is called for. In whatever form, written correspondence that is properly formatted, grammatically correct and which effectively conveys your thoughts is an important component in the success of your work life. Not only is the ability to write well a valuable asset, it is often essential given the specialized work that is often performed.

Purpose

Types of official correspondence include e-mail, internal memoranda, business letters, letters of reference, letters of introduction, notes and reports. While the substance of these documents varies, all serve the purpose of communicating thought. That thought may be to inform, to initiate or record an activity. Unlike direct verbal communication, the sender of a written document does not have real-time feedback from the recipient and, thus, the writer must be reasonably certain that the intended thought is clearly elucidated.

The type of document that is used depends on how formal or official the content and whether the document is being sent internally or outside of the organization. A uniformed service letter often conveys a sense of formality that may be warranted when writing about a technical subject and/or to a very high ranking officer. A memorandum is less formal in the sense that it may include acronyms that are commonly used in the organization, although the memorandum format may be more standardized than a letter. Military services typically have guidelines that govern how correspondence is to be constructed with regard to format, common elements and content.

Appearance & Stationery

The overall appearance of official documents may influence a reader's perception of the sender and how the message is received. Factors which combine to form a paper document's appearance include the stationery used, neatness, and format of those elements that comprise the document. The use of text embellishments such as character bolding or headings can enhance the appearance as well as readability of many documents.

Official stationery is ordinarily prescribed with regard to the use of letterhead and print characteristics. Paper should be of good quality bond, with a basis weight of 20 or 22 lb. Standard Business and up to 24 lb. Executive, with a rag/fiber content of at least 25%. Paper comes in various sizes, but most frequently in standard sizes of 8½" by 11" Standard, and 7¼" by 10½" Executive for hand- or computer-written correspondence that is more personal in nature. Corresponding envelopes are commonly Commercial No. 10, 4⅛" by 9½", requiring two parallel folds of the business letter; and Executive, 3⅞" by 7½", requiring two parallel folds. Envelopes also come in the standard size of 3⅝" by 6½" for very brief notes.

Composition

Well written communications include those that are logically constructed, keeping in mind the purpose and intent. For lengthy documents, an outline is useful in organizing your thoughts – concepts may be arranged from the most to least important, chronologically, or in some other systematic approach. The outline should begin with the purpose of the communication and lead to a clear conclusion, recommendation or call for action. Determine the need for a review of background material or research on a subject, and accomplish this task before proceeding further; the outline is then revised accordingly. Organize the thoughts you want to convey in a logical progression. State the more salient points early and provide any supporting material. Sentences should be clear and concise, grammatically correct and have no spelling errors. Word selection and usage are important – a conversational style is usually considered best, avoiding multisyllabic or overly technical terms and stilted phraseology. Review/revise the draft as often as necessary until satisfactory.

A critical aspect of any document is the tone it conveys. Business and uniformed service correspondence that has a professional, yet friendly tone is generally better received and more effective in achieving its intended objective. All documents should convey a sense of credibility and an interest in the reader's perspective. E-mail and interoffice memoranda provide an efficient method of transmitting ideas to your colleagues, and may be less formal and more to the point that a business letter.

Official correspondence has specified elements which, for letters and memoranda, are compared and summarized on the next page.

Letter and Memoranda Elements

LETTER	MEMORANDUM*
Date	Date: line
Inside address	To: line
No From: line	From: line
Subject introduced in first paragraph	Subject: line
Salutation	*No* salutation
Indent paragraphs of text	Left justify all text
Complimentary close	*No* complimentary close
Signature	Signature
Signature block	*No* signature block

Align left margin with centerline of the letterhead seal.

Letter Elements (see Letter Elements in Composite Letter, next page)
There are standard elements to official correspondence.

Date. Uniformed services use the sequence of day-month-year, without punctuation, for intra-service, inter-service and certain governmental letters and memoranda (e.g., 15 October 2025 *or* 15 Oct 25). When corresponding with a non-uniformed service entity, the standard business sequence of month-day,-year is used (e.g., October 15, 2025).

Declarations/Notations (optional). Special mailing declarations and on-arrival notations are next, placed flush with the left margin, entirely capitalized (e.g., REGISTERED MAIL, or CONFIDENTIAL).

Inside Address. The inside address should begin with the person's full name, preceded by an honorific (e.g., CDR, Dr., Mr., Ms.), or, followed by an academic or professional degree with no honorific. The person's position title, duty station or business name, and address follow on successive lines. If addressed to an institution and an attention line is needed, place it on the line following the duty station/company name. The envelope is addressed the same as the inside address.

Subject. In an official letter, the subject is introduced in the first paragraph. If needed for referencing purposes, however, place a subject line before the salutation. Words such as Subject:, Reference:, RE:, or Re: may be used.

Salutation. The salutation "Dear" plus an honorific – a person's personal or professional title (may abbreviate), or uniformed service rank/title spelled out – and addressee's surname is standard. When on a first name basis, the writer may use "Dear" and the person's given name. Note, however, that for form letters and when a higher ranking commissioned officer writes to a lower rank officer who is well known to the senior officer, the sender may instead line-out the recipient's typewritten surname and handwrite that officer's given name above the surname.

Text. The body of a letter is single spaced, with one space between paragraphs. For brief letters, one and one-half or double spacing can be used. A minimum of two or three lines of text warrant a continuation sheet. There are a number of formats used for continuation sheets. Among the more complete is placing "Page" and page number flush left at the top of the page, followed with a spaced hyphen and the addressee's honorific and name: *Page 2 - LT Thomas Kelly*

Complimentary Close. The complimentary close is placed about two lines below the text. Uniformed service personnel may customarily close written correspondence with "Respectfully," when senior officers write to junior personnel, or "Very respectfully," when junior officers correspond with senior officers. When less formality is acceptable, officers can abbreviate and use "R", "V/R" or "V/r". There are other polite closes for a business letter; for example:

Formal: *Very respectfully yours, Respectfully yours, Very truly yours,*

Less Formal: *Very sincerely yours, Sincerely yours, Most Sincerely,   Sincerely,*

Informal and Personal: *Cordially yours, Kind regards, Best regards/wishes, Regards,*

Signature Block. The signature block is aligned vertically with, and placed three to five lines below the complimentary close. The writer's name and academic and/or professional credentials are placed on the first line. In business, the writer's position title follows on the second line, whereas in the uniformed services, the writer's rank and service designation are placed on the second line, with position title on the third line. For uniformed service memoranda, the abbreviated rank and service designation should be on the second line (with the position title placed at the top of memoranda in the 'From:' line).

Closing Data. Attachment or enclosure information is placed flush with the left margin, after the signature block.

COMPOSITE   **DEPARTMENT OF HEALTH & HUMAN SERVICES**
MODIFIED   **WASHINGTON, DC 20201**
BLOCK LETTER   July 15, 2025   ◀ **Date**

Katherine Smith, M.D.
National Cancer Institute   ◀ **Inside Address**
9000 Rockville Pike
Bethesda, MD 20894

Dear Dr. Smith: ◀ **Salutation**

This is to confirm my presentation on Promoting the Nation's Health, to be given at the National Cancer Institute on July 27, 2025.

Complementary Close ▶   Sincerely,
                                 Richard H. Johnston
Signature Block ▶   Richard H. Johnston, M.D., M.P.H.
                                 Vice Admiral, U.S. Public Health Service
                                 United States Surgeon General

---

Letter Formats (see *Composite Modified Block Letter,* above)

There are several commonly used formats for preparing an official letter.

Full Block Form. The full block form of a letter simply means that all letter elements, discussed above, are begun flush with the left margin.

Modified Block Form. This form follows the full block form, except that the date, complimentary close and signature begin at the center or right-of-center.

Modified Semi-Block Form. This form follows the modified block form, except that the first word of each paragraph of the text is indented.

Executive Form. This uses the modified semi-block format, except that the inside address, flush left, is placed below the signature block.

Greetings & Introductions

Refer also to Chapter Three, Uniformed Service Courtesy & Protocol.

Upon first meeting someone, the impression you convey impacts significantly on your future relationship. It is therefore important in dealing with uniformed service personnel, business associates and the public that you greet and address them, and make introductions cordially and properly.

Addressing Others

As a general rule, persons whom you first meet should be addressed by an honorific such as Mr., Ms., Mrs., or with a person's rank or professional title such as Commander, Doctor, Reverend, Senator, and the person's surname (last name). You should continue to address a person in this manner until he/she says that you may use their given (first) name or you become familiar enough with each other that use of the first name is acceptable. Within most organizations, first names are used among employees, with a title and person's last name reserved for more senior persons by age or executive rank. If you are on a first name basis and see a senior colleague accompanied by an outside person, however, you should address the colleague by rank or title and his last name.

The terms "sir" and "ma'am" are proper forms of address within the uniformed services. "Madam" and "Madame" are appropriate as a title in officialdom (e.g., "Madam Chairperson") and in addressing untitled women who are citizens in certain other countries. Refer to the table "Forms of Address", below, for proper forms of verbal/written address for civilian government officials.

Greetings

You should rise, step toward a visitor and remain standing when greeting or being introduced to that person. Similarly, when other than your co-workers, stand and welcome visitors and senior officials to your office.

Greet the other person cordially, with a pleasant demeanor. If you already know the person, something such as "How are you?" is said, and you may want to shake hands. Unless you are close personal friends, your response to such a greeting should be limited to something like "Fine, thanks, and you?" even if you are not doing very well. When being introduced to someone new, offer your hand in a comfortably firm handshake – a man need not wait for a woman to first offer her hand, as was previously the custom. If the palm of your hand is moist, subtly wipe it dry before a handshake. Ordinarily, a glove is removed prior to shaking hands.

After introductions are made, persons should say a few words of greeting to one another, such as "How do you do?" or "It's nice to meet you." A few pleasantries help to relax everyone, and any business should be initiated only after all participants have been seated and given a few minutes to become accustomed to the surroundings.

Introductions

Making proper introductions is an important, life-long ability that should come naturally. Whether at a meeting or social function, all officers should be able to render this courtesy as a sign of cordiality and respect. The proper manner of making introductions can be remembered if a few guidelines are kept in mind. You should introduce:

- a lower ranking person *to* a higher ranking person;
- a business colleague *to* a client or an outside associate;
- a younger person *to* an older person;
- a family member *to* a business associate or colleague;
- all else being equal, a man *to* a woman.

The simplest way is to always begin with the name of the person who has the higher precedence. It is also important to include a position title or other meaningful information about a person when you are making introductions. Here are two options.

- Admiral Whitower, I would like you to meet Captain Brad Collins, the Director of Human Resources. Captain Collins, this is Admiral Whitower, our Surgeon General.

Alternatively, reverse the order and utilize 'you' with the preposition 'to.'

- Captain Collins, may I introduce *you to* Admiral Whitower, the Surgeon General.

At sponsored functions, it is normally the host's responsibility to greet and introduce people. If a person's name is not clearly heard, you should ask that the name be repeated. If the person making introductions errs in introducing you, it is usually a good idea to affably correct the mistake; and, if you perceive that the person has forgotten your name or you are not introduced, you should introduce yourself to the others present.

Always introduce an acquaintance whom only you know, if that person is with you or joins you during a group conversation. When introducing a spouse, use his/her first name (e.g., "Lieutenant Walsh, I would like you to meet my husband, Doug"). If you forget a person's name while making introductions and that person does not introduce himself, apologetically (but without embarrassment) admit the lapse of recall.

Introductions in a receiving line are the responsibility of the host, the guest who is queued in the waiting line, and/or a staff person assigned to facilitate introductions. At larger functions, when as a guest you may not be readily known by the host, you introduce yourself giving your name and identifier information (e.g., organizational position and affiliation). If a staff person is assisting, he will greet you, take your name and introduce you to the host who, in turn, introduces you to the next person receiving you or a guest of honor, if present. As the host, you should greet guests with a smile, a warm handshake and a pleasant remark.

Forms of Address

Proper forms of address to use for civilian government officials are given in the following table.

FORMS OF ADDRESS
CIVILIAN GOVERNMENT OFFICIALS*

PERSON	WRITTEN ADDRESS	SALUTATION	CONVERSATION
FEDERAL			
President	The President The White House	Dear Mr. President	Mr. President or Sir
Vice-President	The Vice-President Old Executive Office Bldg.	Dear Mr. Vice-President	Mr. Vice-President or Mr. Clark or Sir
Cabinet Member	The Honorable David Clark Secretary of HHS	Dear Mr. Secretary or Dear Sir	Mr. Secretary or Secretary Clark or Mr. Clark
Senator	The Honorable David Clark U.S. Senate	Dear Senator Clark or Dear Sir	Senator or Senator Clark
Representative	The Honorable David Clark U.S. House of Representatives	Dear Mr. Clark or Dear Sir	Mr. Clark or Representative Clark
House Speaker	The Honorable David Clark Speaker of the House of Representatives	Dear Mr. Speaker or Dear Sir	Mr. Speaker or Mr. Clark
Chief Justice	The Chief Justice The Supreme Court	Dear Mr. Chief Justice or Dear Sir	Mr. Chief Justice or Sir
Associate Justice	Mr. Justice Clark The Supreme Court	Dear Mr. Justice or Dear Justice Clark or Dear Sir	Mr. Justice or Justice Clark or Sir
Ambassador	The Honorable David Clark American Ambassador	Dear Mr. Ambassador or Dear Ambassador Clark or Dear Sir	Mr. Ambassador or Ambassador Clark or Mr. Clark or Sir
STATE/LOCAL			
Governor	The Honorable David Clark Governor of Rhode Island	Dear Governor or Dear Governor Clark or Dear Sir	Governor or Governor Clark or Sir
Senator	The Honorable David Clark Rhode Island Senate	Dear Senator Clark or Dear Sir	Senator or Senator Clark; or Sir
Mayor	The Honorable David Clark Mayor of Newport	Dear Mr. Mayor or Mayor Clark; or Dear Sir	Mr. Mayor or Mayor Clark or Your Honor
Judge	The Honorable David Clark Judge, Superior Court	Dear Judge Clark	Mr. Justice or Judge Clark

* Substitute "Madam" in place of "Mr." or "Sir" for a woman official.

Presentations & Speaking

Speaking ability has the potential to influence the perception of others about a person's background, competence, or other impressionistic factor. Officers should therefore work, if needed, on developing their conversational, professional and/or presentation skills. Most commissioned officers will be called upon to make prepared presentations during their career. In order to effectively present the message, whether it is to present information or inspire action, officers need to optimize their preparation, delivery and stage presence. This is essential in establishing yourself as a credible spokesperson and in advancing ideas that enlighten and/or persuade those in attendance.

Preparation

It is very important to thoroughly prepare before any presentation.

* Your presentation should be well organized by having a clear introduction and purpose or thesis, a body that focuses on the salient points you want to make, and an ending that summarizes the main points and conclusions.
* Memorable content is logically and concisely constructed, and utilizes specific examples and data to illustrate and support your statements. Avoid rambling thoughts and unsupported commentaries.
* The language you use should be kept relatively simple, and terminology should be readily understandable to the audience.
* Practice your presentation in front of a mirror and record it, if possible. Listen carefully for voice characteristics; you will want to articulate words with good diction and an agreeable pitch, tonal quality, tempo or rate of speech, and volume of sound. Observe body movements – notice your posture, facial expressiveness, and arm and hand gestures. Work on problem areas and re-record yourself to determine if improvements are evident. If possible, conduct a "dry run" in the presence of a colleague.
* If you are using slides or other visual aids, incorporate them into your practice session. Make sure the visuals are properly sequenced and correspond with what you are saying, that they truly add substance to the presentation, are professional in appearance, and are large enough to be read at the back of the meeting room.
* Ensure that you finish the presentation within set time constraints.
* If not already known, familiarize yourself with the background and expectations of the audience so that, with this knowledge, you are more comfortable when speaking before them.
* Visit the meeting room beforehand to familiarize yourself with the setting and check on the working order and use of audiovisual equipment.
* Finally, use mental imagery to visualize yourself making the presentation, effectively and with confidence. Visualize this as a positive experience.

Delivery
While the style of delivery may vary, some general guidelines follow.

- Take a slow, deep breath and mentally calm yourself. Begin by thanking the person who introduced you and, if appropriate, greeting distinguished guests, including senior officers of note, and then the audience.
- Establish rapport with the audience. For instance, open with remarks or a humorous anecdote that relates yourself or the subject of the presentation with the audience or the meeting location.
- Use proper grammar and a good working vocabulary that is natural and suited to your personal style. Avoid the following: hesitations; filler words or phrases such as "uh" or "you know;" slang or words that are of passing fashion; and lingo or technical jargon unless appropriate for the audience.
- Unless giving a formal speech, it is usually best to use an outline of key thoughts and phrases, rather than utilize a complete manuscript. Highlighting or margin notes on the outline can be helpful in identifying places in the presentation where pauses or more verbal emphasis is indicated.
- Visually, you should slowly pan over the audience, breaking regularly to make eye contact with individual members of the audience.
- Your voice should be confident and well-modulated. Avoid being mono-tonal. Appropriate variations in pitch, tempo and volume of your voice make your thoughts more convincing and interesting to listen to.
- When using visual aids, use a pointer to indicate specific items on the visual that correspond with the content of your presentation, and speak to the audience (not toward the visual) whenever possible.
- If you take audience questions in a large room without the benefit of floor microphones, you should repeat the question so that everyone may hear it.
- End the presentation on a "solid" and/or uplifting note.

Stage Presence
There are certain tips that may be helpful to keep in mind.

- Aside from greater visibility, standing and/or using a podium will impart more authority, control and formality to the meeting.
- Good body language is particularly important. Confidence and poise are conveyed by projecting a calm and friendly facial disposition, and maintaining an erect, but relaxed posture. Gesturing of the arms and hands is very effective if it is natural, sincere and not overdone. Avoid nervous mannerisms such as fidgeting with your hands.
- Avoid having pocket coins or jewelry that might jingle when you move. When you are about to cough or sneeze, cover your mouth with a handkerchief and turn your head away from the audience and microphone.
- An authoritative, professional appearance is important. You should always be well groomed and dressed in proper uniform that is clean and pressed.

Introducing the Speaker

The introduction of a speaker should be brief and upbeat. As the introducer, you should acquaint the audience with the speaker, mentioning significant aspects of his/her background and accomplishments (personalize this information when possible). Relate the reason for, or content of the presentation to the audience and pique their interest in what the speaker is about to say.

Immediately following the address, thank the speaker and comment on the excellence (informative nature, etc.) of the presentation. If this also concludes the program, thank the audience for their attendance at the function.

Telecommunications

E-mail, cell phone and telephone manners have a decided impact on the perception of others about one's professionalism and organization. Communications that are utilized intelligently and professionally show that you have respect for the other person and value their time.

Electronic Mail

E-mail is probably the leading method for daily communications due to its convenience and efficiency. While a telephone conversation has the advantage of being interactive, it is also clear that some individuals prefer a less personal approach to communicate, and e-mail fulfills that preference, as well. When using e-mail, keep in mind the following.

- Use Appropriately – Unless necessary for archival purposes, e-mail is not recommended for very lengthy, complex or confidential information. Know when to opt for sending a properly formatted document, which is usually perceived as more respectful or holding more importance; or, to opt for talking by telephone or in person with the intended recipient.
- Use Discretion – E-mail is legally considered government property when utilized on the job and, thus, there is no privacy protection. When composing an e-mail, be mindful that an e-mail is a permanent record that can readily be forwarded to others and lacks assurance of confidentiality.
- Be Clear and Professional – Begin an e-mail by stating the purpose and ensure that it conveys the message you intend, because you do not have the benefit of real time feedback from the recipient. The content should always be professional – respectful, polite and friendly in tone.
- Use Uniformed Service Protocol – When sending an e-mail to service personnel, use proper salutations and closings, as appropriate.
- Check Content – An e-mail reflects upon the sender, so always review the content of the e-mail and use the computer spelling and grammar check features before sending it. Delay sending an e-mail if there is any doubt about the content and/or further consideration may be indicated.

Cellular/Smart Phone

Cell phones are a great technological advance and have become ubiquitous our daily lives. When used properly and with consideration for others, a cell phone provides ready connectivity that is important in the business world. However, when used without regard for others, cell phone use can be an annoyance that may convey disrespect and reflect poorly upon the user. The following are some tips to keep in mind.

- Be Considerate – Do not place or receive cell phone calls in the presence of others at the office, during business meetings or presentations, or at business meals. Turn off the phone or use the silent mode in those instances, and in enclosed public places such as auditoriums, theaters, and places of worship. Do not view/send e-mail and text messages, or browse the Web on a smart phone during business meetings and presentations.
- Use Appropriately – Avoid taking nonofficial calls in the presence of others when on duty time. If you must take a personal call in such settings, however, excuse yourself to a location away from others and keep your phone conversation brief.
- Use Discretion – Do not conduct business discussions on the cell phone in places such as elevators or in close proximity to others in public areas such as airports where the conversation can be easily overheard by others.

Telephone

- Answering – Answer the office telephone by the third ring with your rank, surname and, if appropriate, title. Before placing a caller on hold, always ask a caller "May I place you on hold," and then check back periodically. If prolonged, ask if the caller would like to continue to hold. When transferring a phone call, give the caller the name of the person and extension number to whom the call is being directed.
- Placing Calls – Whenever possible, place your own calls, especially to senior officials. If you expect a lengthy discussion, give the purpose of your call and ask if the other person has sufficient time at the moment. If using a speakerphone, inform the person being called and identify any other persons in the room with you. When ending an official call, thank the other person by rank (if appropriate) and name. If disconnected, it is the caller's responsibility to call back, regardless of the cause.
- Conference Calls – Be present early so that conferees can be connected ahead of time, and begin by introducing yourself and others in the room if not already done. If there is background noise or you need to speak to colleagues in the room off-record, use the mute button on the telephone.
- Other Guidelines – Return calls promptly within the same day. Remember that your conversational ability and professionalism will largely determine how you are perceived by others. If going to someone's office and that person is on the telephone, do not enter unless you are motioned in.

CHAPTER EIGHT

MEETINGS

Meetings are endemic in government and the uniformed services, as well as in business. Meetings take many forms and are called for various purposes. They support the communication needs of an organization and are a forum for participants. The effectiveness of a meeting relates directly to the skills of the chairperson and those in attendance. This chapter provides guidance on optimizing the effectiveness of meetings.

THE CHAIRPERSON

THE PARTICIPANTS

OFFICE APPOINTMENTS

CONVENTIONS

PARLIAMENTARY PROCEDURE

Effective meetings that are productive and a good utilization of participants' time are essential to proper management of a corporate entity. Meetings are called for the purpose of planning activities, briefings, providing information, solving problems, making decisions, or a combination thereof. Types of meetings include the impromptu meeting in a colleague's office, appointments or scheduled meetings with others, regular policy or staff meetings, interdepartmental meetings, briefings, senior official meetings, and so on.

While the person who conducts a meeting is usually the most visible, each person at the meeting is on view. As a participant and an officer, you are compared to, and evaluated by those in attendance on the basis of your mannerisms, how you think, and generally how you handle yourself and interact with others. In other words, you are judged on the basis of personal qualities and professional competence. Meetings are therefore important in not only furthering your work and the organization's mission, but they can be an important determinant in whether you advance and achieve your career potential within the Commissioned Corps.

The Chairperson

The person who leads a meeting sets the direction and tone of the proceedings, and has the responsibility to exercise control in a way that fosters and maintains productive communication among the participants. The degree of control will depend on the meeting purpose, agenda and attendees. For the uninitiated, this can be a challenge when controversial issues are before the group, while giving due deference to senior officials. It is therefore important that the chairperson be capable and knowledgeable, and someone in whom the participants have confidence. There are certain things to keep in mind when chairing a meeting.

Pre-Meeting

- There should be a clear reason or purpose for calling the meeting. Formulate well-defined objectives and reasonable outcomes to be met. Select the persons to be invited as meeting participants, accordingly.
- Schedule the meeting at a convenient location, date and time, with an ending time. The meeting room should be of a size that will comfortably accommodate the participants and is otherwise conducive to the conduct of a productive meeting.
- When the type of meeting or number of discussion items calls for it, prepare an agenda with the topics prioritized so that the more important items are scheduled first. Send the agenda and background information to participants in advance of the meeting, indicating, where applicable, the staff member(s) who will lead the discussion on an agenda item. When planning a general staff meeting, provide the participants an opportunity to suggest items for the agenda before it is finalized.
- Any audiovisual equipment should be set up in advance of the meeting.
- Designate someone, usually a junior officer, to prepare official minutes or notes of the meeting, but remember that it is also good practice for the chairperson to write down important points during the meeting with which to compare the draft minutes of record.

During the Meeting

- Arrive early to greet attendees, particularly if outside guests and/or senior officials are participants. Begin the meeting on time. However, for special meetings or those with outside guests and/or senior officials as participants, delay the starting time a few minutes if those individuals or other key participants are not yet present.
- Introduce participants, as appropriate. State the purpose and objectives of the meeting, and announce the scheduled ending time.
- Facilitate and encourage open discussion of issues. Show interest and elicit further discussion by posing questions and highlighting or rephras-

ing significant points. Tactfully deter those who begin to dominate the proceedings and call on other persons who might have knowledge of the subject. Show patience and impartiality in dealing with participants.

- Keep participants on track with the agenda, in terms of topics, objectives and time of the meeting. Periodically summarize the discussions during lengthy proceedings. If tangential issues are brought up, it is better to postpone deliberation on the matter unless there is concurrence that the new subject is pertinent and should be discussed. If it appears that insufficient time has been allotted to cover all agenda items, stop and discuss possible options (e.g., items that should be discussed, referred to a committee, or postponed).

- At the conclusion of the meeting, summarize the discussions and results. Recap follow-up actions to be taken, the persons responsible and time frame for completion. Thank the participants for their attendance and important contributions to the meeting. Distribute meeting minutes and/or action documents within a few days to all participants.

The Participants

Meeting participants also have responsibilities that help produce a more effective meeting. Keep in mind that commissioned officers are expected to be leaders, and you can only lead by thoughtfully articulating your ideas.

Pre-Meeting

- Be ready in advance of the meeting. Know the purpose and objectives of the meeting. Review the agenda and any provided background materials.
- If an issue suggests the possibility of discord, prepare yourself mentally to deal with any conflict in a professional way.
- When making a presentation, experts agree that it is better to write down and present from key thoughts, rather than read from a manuscript. (See the Section, *Presentations & Speaking*.)
- Ensure that any hand-out materials have a professional appearance.

During the Meeting

- Place cell/smart phones on silent mode before entering the room. Be on time – it is distracting to arrive when the meeting is in progress and suggests a lack of respect, even if that is not the case.
- If you are a newcomer to a regularly held meeting, allow others to take their seats before seating yourself. Be cognizant that the organization may reserve what are termed "power" or authority positions (e.g., the head and foot of the conference table, the immediate right and left of the head position, center chairs) for senior officials.

- Stay on focus, be attentive and speak-up, but do not dominate a discussion. The effectiveness of a meeting is realized only when the participants maintain interest and active involvement in the discussions – stay alert and express your viewpoints.
- Generally, there is no reason to ever view/send e-mail and text messages on your smart phone during a business meeting, which is considered disrespectful. If you are bored, avoid displaying poor habits such as disengaging from discussions, whispering to your neighbor, or doodling.
- Be considerate of the thoughts and feelings of others. Because people perceive matters differently or are not versed in the nuances of all subject matters, any derision of others is generally out of place in a meeting. Do not personalize negative remarks. When on the receiving end of an unduly negative comment, do not respond in kind; keep reactive emotions under control.

Office Appointments

One-on-one and small group meetings held in an individual's office may afford the opportunity of discussing a matter in better detail, but the effectiveness of those meetings can be side tracked if a few courtesies are overlooked. Therefore, be alert to the following.

- Be on time, whether the host or attendee. If the meeting is held in your office, do not let prior meetings overrun their allotted time. If you must keep others waiting outside your office, inform them of the approximate time delay and ensure their comfort.
- For colleagues and outside attendees coming to your office, stand and welcome those attendees, offering a handshake. Introduce meeting participants to each other, including individuals' names and affiliations, and gesture to be seated. If you an attendee and no one in the host group introduces you, extend your hand to those nearby, shake hands and introduce yourself. Business cards may be exchanged at this time.
- If you are the host, offer the group refreshments and make a few, brief pleasantries, if appropriate, prior to starting discussions.
- Once the meeting has begun, do not receive telephone calls; attendees should have cell phones turned to silent mode or off. Listen attentively, ask questions and take notes. Show proper deference to senior officials (this should not, however, deter discussion of an issue). If you are leading the discussion, summarize the proceedings at the conclusion of the meeting and reiterate any agreed upon action items.
- If you are the host, thank the visiting attendees (attendees should also thank the chairperson), exchange handshakes and escort visitors out.

Conventions

Conventions include professional association meetings and other large meetings that PHS officers attend on a periodic basis. These meetings offer professional and uniformed service-related education, information and training that is often essential for professional licensure and for remaining current on new professional practice and Commissioned Corps issues. There may also be an exhibitor area for company and government sponsored display booths covering a myriad of products, programs and services of interest to attendees. Conventions provide a networking opportunity that is important in keeping up with acquaintances and learning about the experiences of colleagues. While there is often a social program, the importance of these meetings is primarily their program sessions. These meetings can be helpful in advancing an officer's career if a few things are kept in mind.

- As a speaker, you need to be professional in every way – thorough preparation in order to speak with authority on the seminar topic; effective presentation skills; and, high quality visuals aids (if used). (See the Section, *Presentations & Speaking*.)
- Review the agenda before each meeting day in order to select the more pertinent seminars that relate to your professional interests. Always be on time, whether the speaker or an attendee. Keep any questions you may have for the speaker brief and to the point.
- Remember that your actions during the business portion of the meeting, at receptions, and after-hours are often in view by colleagues and fellow officers. Even when seminars may not be that interesting, it is important to fulfill your responsibility to attend needed educational sessions when meeting costs are paid by your office. At other times, it is important to maintain good behavior, because your actions reflect on you *and* the USPHS/HHS.

Parliamentary Procedure

Knowledge of parliamentary procedure is essential if you are the presiding officer or are a delegate to a voting assembly of a large organization. The standard book on this subject is *Robert's Rules of Order Revised*. It is noteworthy that this book was originally written in 1876, with a revised edition in 1915, by General Henry M. Robert, a West Point graduate who became Chief of Engineers, U.S. Army. The book can be obtained at book stores. Following is a brief review of some basic rules.

Motions

There are different motions, classified according to their purpose, that are used to conduct the business of a meeting.

Main Motion. The main motion brings forward a new topic for consideration. A member is first recognized by the presiding officer in order to make the motion, which must be seconded by another member. When first proposed, it is a *motion,* but is thereafter referred to by the chairperson as the *question.* The chairperson restates the motion and asks if there are any remarks, at which time debate may proceed. Only one main motion may be considered at a time, and all remarks are addressed to the chairperson. A member may seek to close debate by moving *the previous question,* but all other motions having an order of precedence greater than this subsidiary motion must be dealt with first.

Subsidiary Motions. Subsidiary motions relate to a specified action on the main motion; they are used for the purpose of modifying or otherwise disposing of the main motion. The subsidiary motion must be considered before further action is taken on the main motion. Subsidiary motions yield in precedence to incidental and privileged motions. There are seven subsidiary motions, with the following precedence: lay on the table; previous question (close debate); limit or extend debate; postpone to a certain time; commit or refer (to a committee); amend; and postpone indefinitely.

Incidental Motions. Incidental motions are incident to the pending question and are dealt with as they arise. Most of these motions are not debatable. Incidental motions yield to privileged motions, but have no order of precedence among themselves. Some incidental motions are as follows: appeal from the decision of the chairperson; consider by paragraph (seriatim); division of the question; parliamentary inquiry; point of information; point of order; suspend the rules; and, withdraw a motion.

Privileged Motions. Privileged motions have no direct connection to the main motion. They are used to take care of relatively urgent matters and therefore have precedence over other types of motions. There are five privileged motions, with the following precedence: fix the time at which to adjourn; adjourn; recess; raise question of privilege; and call for orders of the day.

Other Motions. There are a few other motions that have the effect of bringing a question back for consideration on the floor. These have particular rules associated with them. They include the following: take from the table; reconsider; and rescind.

Precedence of Motions

Precedence sets the priority by which motions are considered. The following list is arranged according to rank, with the highest precedence at the top of the list. Privileged and subsidiary motions have precedence within their own categories, whereas incidental motions have no order of precedence within the category. Note that the main motion is ranked last – other motions are made while the main motion is pending, and those must be dealt with before the main motion.

Privileged Motions
[By order of precedence.]

Fix the time at which to adjourn
Adjourn
Take recess
Raise question of privilege
Call for orders of the day

Incidental Motions
[No order of precedence.]

Appeal from the decision of the chairperson*
Consider by paragraph
Division of the question
Parliamentary inquiry
Point of information
Point of order
Suspend the rules
Withdraw a motion

Subsidiary Motions
[By order of precedence.]

Lay on the table
Previous question (close debate)
Limit or extend debate
Postpone to a certain time*
Commit or refer (to a committee)*
Amend the amendment*
Amend the main motion*
Postpone indefinitely*

Main Motion*

* Motions that are debatable.

Officers are advised to refer to *Robert's Rules of Order Revised* for more detailed information.

CHAPTER NINE

TABLE PROTOCOL

Knowledge of dining etiquette is considered basic to an officer's social abilities. It is a generally held belief that dining skills reflect upbringing. In business, as the term is broadly applied, proficiency at the dining table can significantly influence the perception of others with respect to a person's professional competence and the organization they represent.

> TABLE SETTINGS
> TABLE MANNERS
> RESTAURANT DINING

Table Settings

All officers should be familiar with the placement and use of dining utensils, china and crystal. Such knowledge, combined with good table manners, is considered a component of an officer's core social skills. A formal multicourse place setting is depicted in Figure 1. Less formal place settings follow the same pattern, but with fewer items than are shown. The formality of the occasion will guide the selection of the selection of flatware, china, crystal and other table items. At a formal dinner, flatware should be silverplate or sterling.

FLATWARE

Placement. Flatware is set with the handle ends about one inch from the edge of the table. It is placed on both sides of the main plate, with forks placed to the left, and knives and spoons to the right. The soup spoon, which may be round (clear soup) or oval (cream soup) is placed to the right of the knives, and a demitasse spoon or teaspoon may be placed to the right of a coffee cup and saucer (or when it is served).

The utensils are arranged in order of use from the outside in, corresponding with the courses of the meal. For example, a salad fork may be located on either side of the dinner fork, depending on when the salad is to be served (i.e., before or, in the European manner, after the main course).

The dessert fork and spoon may be placed above the main plate, as in Figure 1, placed in the inside positions of the forks and spoons or brought to the table when dessert is served.

Figure 1. Formal Place Setting *[In this setting, salad fork is in European position.]*

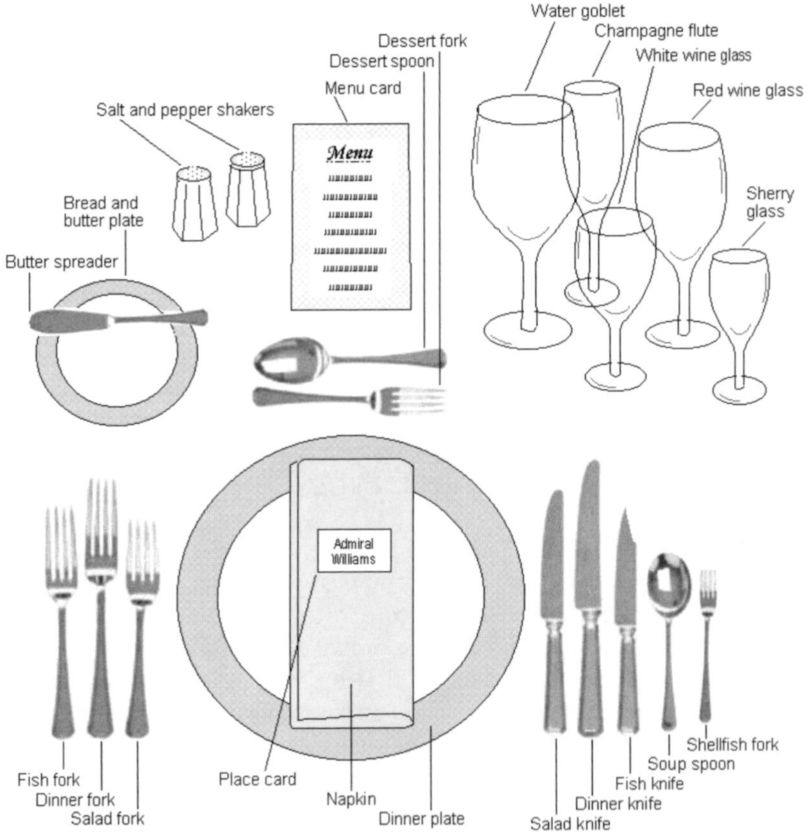

With the exception of the addition of an oyster/shellfish fork placed to the right of the spoon(s), there are never more than three forks and/or three knives in the place setting. If another fork or knife is needed, it is placed on the table when the course is served. Note that knife blades always face toward the plate. The butter knife or spreader is placed straight, or at a slight diagonal from upper left to lower right, across the top rim of the butter plate, with the blade facing inward.

Use of Utensils. The *soup spoon* should be spooned away from you, inside the bowl. Sip the soup from the side of the spoon (i.e., not from the tip). Used spoons are placed on the saucer or under plate of the dish, or may be placed in the bowl if it is shallow.

American and Continental Methods. There are two methods for handling a fork and knife, referred to as the American and Continental styles – both styles are acceptable in the U.S., with the Continental style becoming more prevalent. In both styles, the fork is held in your left hand, tines pointing down, to hold the food in place, and the knife is held in your right hand to cut it. In the *American style,* the knife is returned to the plate and the fork is transferred to the right hand, tines up, to pick up the piece of food. In the *Continental style,* the fork remains in the left hand and, with tines still down, the piece of food is conveyed by fork to your mouth; the knife remains in your right hand as long as needed. Those who are left-handed hold the utensils in their opposite hand, whichever method is used. Whichever style is used, when the

fork is in the left hand with tines pointing down, the index finger should extend over the shaft (Figure 2). The fork
handle should *not* be held as if it were
a pencil, and never be gripped in the
palm of your hand at a 90° angle to
the dinner plate.

Figure 2. Holding the Fork

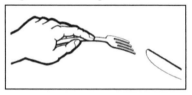

While not being used, a knife is placed diagonally across the upper right edge of the plate, blade facing the center of the plate. *If you are not finished eating and want to pause,* leave the knife diagonally across the upper right edge of the plate and place the fork in a parallel position, tines up and centered on the plate. Alternatively, use the European style, crossing the fork, tines down, handle lower left, over the knife, handle lower right to the center of the plate.

When finished eating, the fork and
knife are customarily placed together
across the middle of the plate, horizontally from right to left or diagonally
from lower right to upper left, knife a-
bove the fork, blade turned inward, and
fork tines up or down (Figure 3).

Figure 3. Finished Position

CHINA

Placement. The place setting may include a service plate (also referred to as a charger or place plate), upon which may be placed the pre-entrée dishes or salad plate. The service plate or the dinner plate is at the center of the place setting, with other place setting items arranged around it (Figure 1). At a formal dinner, a salad plate will not be present when there is a separate salad course.

Use. When the main course is served, the service plate (if present) will be replaced with a dinner plate, with or without the entrée served on it. At a less formal dinner where salad and/or butter plates are absent, the dinner plate may be used for salad, butter and bread. A bread/roll can be placed on the dinner plate, or, on the tablecloth if it is *unbuttered.* A soup bowl should be tipped away from you to spoon out residual liquid. Serving dishes are passed around the table to the right (counterclockwise). When passing a dish to another person, hold the serving dish so that a handle of the dish and serving utensils are readily available for the other diner to grasp.

CRYSTAL

Placement. Glassware is located above and toward the right of the dinner plate (Figure 1). Glassware may consist of the water goblet/tumbler, plus other glasses depending on the dinner courses to be served. Each glass has a particular shape and is arranged in the order of use, from right to left, and may include: a sherry glass (for certain soups); white wine glass (typically for a fish course or, absent the sherry glass, sometimes with soup); red wine glass; and, champagne glass (for the entire dinner, or dessert, and toasting).

Use. A water goblet or other large stem glass is held at the base of its bowl, and a tumbler near its base. A wine glass should be held by its stem to keep the glass unsmudged, and to help keep chilled wines (champagne, white wine) remain cool. Your mouth should be empty and lips clean before drinking from crystal to avoid leaving food particles on the rim.

CONDIMENT SERVERS

Placement. Condiments should be transferred from their package containers to serving dishes. There may be a salt and pepper set for every one to three diners. Occasionally, salt cellars or pepper pots (small open bowls with spoons), or pepper mills are provided instead of shakers.

Use. Depending on the formality of the meal, condiments will either be offered by a waiter or placed on the table. Generally, a small amount of each condiment is placed on your butter or dinner plate, as appropriate, and not directly on the food for which it is intended.

NAPKINS

Placement. Napkins are usually folded into a rectangle or chevron style. They are placed on the table in the main plate area or on the service plate. If the first course is in place when diners arrive at the table, the napkin is located to the left of the forks.

Use. Upon being seated at a table, unfold the napkin and place it on your lap. If the dinner is hosted, wait until after the host has placed the napkin on his/her lap. In using the napkin, the mouth should be patted or only lightly wiped. At the end of the meal, the napkin is neatly gathered (*not* re-folded) and placed on the table to the left of the place setting, or in the center area if the dinnerware has been removed.

PLACE CARDS/MENU CARDS

At larger functions or when guest ranking is needed, place cards may be used to indicate where individuals are to be seated. Place cards and menu cards are normally white or cream color, with or without a gold or silver border. They can be handwritten, typed or printed and, at a uniformed service event, lettering is in black ink.

Place Cards. Place cards are up to 3½" wide by 2" high, and are laid flat on the table above the place setting or on the folded napkin on the service plate. Folded place cards are up to 3" high after folding in half, and are placed on the table above the service plate. For more formal occasions, only an officer's rank and surname are written. If two officers have the same last name, their full names are written on the cards.

Menu Cards. Menu cards are up to 5" wide by 7" high. They are set on the table or upright in a holder, centered above each place setting; or, they may be leaned against the glassware, placed on the folded napkin on the service plate, or set on the table between every two diners.

CENTERPIECE AND CANDLES

A centerpiece comprised of flowers or other decorative arrangement is placed at the middle of the table. It should be low enough or very thin (e.g., tall clear glass vase) to permit diners to see each other across the table. If candlesticks or candelabra are used, they are placed at the midpoints between the centerpiece and each end of the table. Candles should be of sufficient height that the flame will stay above eye level. The candles are lighted prior to seating diners and should remain lit until guests have departed. Candlesticks (in contrast to small or votive candles) are not appropriate for the luncheon table but, if present, should be for decorative purposes only and not lit.

SEATING ARRANGEMENTS

For a formal dinner hosted by husband and wife, the host and hostess sit at opposite ends of the table. If female and male guests are equal in number, seating is alternated female-male along the table, noting that spouses are usually not seated beside each other. Consideration should also be given to seating a left-handed guest at a left corner, in order to prevent elbow bumping with the person to his left.

Occasionally, the purpose of the function or the stature of table guests warrants ranked seating. When ranking of guests is involved, seating is begun with the female guest of honor and next most important female to the host's right and left, respectively; and the male guest of honor and next most important male to the hostess' right and left, respectively. (See also the Sections, *Official Dinners & Receptions,* and, *Restaurant Dining.*)

Table Manners

Table manners should be learned to the extent that they become a natural part of one's behavior, without having to think of the "rules." This section should be reviewed along with the sections, *Table Settings* and *Restaurant Dining*.

BEFORE THE MEAL

Whether a business/uniformed service luncheon or professional meeting banquet, certain protocol should be followed. Upon being seated at the table, sit in the chair with your back posture comfortably erect. Unfold the napkin (large napkins may remain half folded) and place it on your lap, with two provisos: if a hosted meal, wait until after the host has begun to place the napkin on his/her lap; and, if an invocation is to be said within a few minutes, the napkin should not be unfolded beforehand. Other than placing the napkin on your lap and taking a sip of water or other beverage, nothing on the table should be disturbed while waiting.

As others arrive at the table, those already seated should stand for face-to-face introductions. Absent such introductions, men need not stand when business, professional or military women colleagues join the table. However, as a courtesy, officers should rise when a flag officer joins the table.

When at the table, do not fidget (e.g., drumming the table with your fingers, touching or combing your hair). While waiting for the meal, in between courses and after the meal, your hands may rest in your lap, hands (at the wrists) may rest on the table edge, or forearms may rest near the table edge.

SERVICE OF THE MEAL

Before or after guests are seated, water glasses are filled. If you notice an item (flatware, china, crystal, napkin) is missing from the place service, ask for the item. If an item is unclean, ask for a replacement – do not clean it yourself.

When a server is present, courses are placed in front of you by the server from the left side. Except for items on your extreme left, dinnerware is removed from the right side when the course is finished. When platters of food are offered by the server, guests should use both the serving fork and spoon to transfer a moderate portion of food to their plates; if a piece of toast is underneath, it is transferred with the food. Also take a portion of any vegetables and garnishes which accompany an entrée on the platter.

At a hosted dinner where a server is not present, food service begins with the person to the host's right and proceeds in that direction (counterclockwise) around the table to the host, who is served last. Diners also pass serving dishes of food and condiments around the table to the right. When an item on the table is out of reach, ask the person nearest the item to "Please pass the (item)." Salt and pepper shakers are passed as a set, even when only one of them is requested. Place a condiment next to, and not on, the food it is to accompany;

gravy and fluid sauces, however, are placed directly on the meat. Foods such as celery and radishes are placed on the butter plate, if present. Bread or rolls will usually be served when the soup or an initial course of salad is served. Where there is no butter plate, an *un*buttered bread or roll may be placed on the tablecloth. Although a salad course may be served after the main course, it is more typically served before or with the entrée. Coffee or tea may be served with the meal, but is more correctly served with, or after, the dessert.

When there is foreign material such as hair or a small insect in food, the material should, it not too unsettling, be removed and the food eaten at a dinner hosted in the home; otherwise, inform the host. In a restaurant, bring it to the server's attention and have the dish replaced.

WINE SERVICE

Wine may be identified as apéritif (appetizer) wines, dinner wines, and after-dinner/dessert wines. Apéritif wines are generally fortified and commonly include the dry sherries and vermouths, or they may be sparkling wines. For the main course, a dry white wine is typically served with fish, a white or light red (blush or rosé) wine is served with poultry and white meat (e.g., pork), and a red wine with wild fowl and red meat. However, it is acceptable to have white, blush or red wine with any food, and serve only one wine, including champagne, as the dinner wine. Dessert wines are often sweeter and most are fortified, and include sweet sherries, ports, sauternes and sweet champagnes. White and blush/rosé wines should be served slightly chilled (about 50° F.), red wines at room temperature (about 70° F.), and sparkling wines well chilled. White wines are opened just before use, whereas a red wine is uncorked one-half to one hour before the meal to permit development of its bouquet.

White wine may be served prior to a first course; otherwise, wine is served when food is brought to the table. The wine will be presented to the host or person who ordered it to review the label to ensure it is the correct wine and vintage. The waiter will remove and place the bottle cork on the table for the host to examine – it should not be dried out. A small amount of wine is then poured into the host's wine glass, who may tip the glass slightly to look for bright color and clarity. He should gently swirl the wine in the glass to release its aroma, sniff and then take a sip of wine to make sure it is alright (has not soured). If satisfactory, he nods approval to the server. If the wine is served at a dinner in the home, the host should check the wine *before* it is brought to the table. The server will pour the wine into each diner's wine glass, about half full (dependent on the glass size), beginning with the person to the host's right and continuing counterclockwise around the table until the host is served.

DURING THE MEAL

In smaller groups, begin eating only after everyone has been served and, if applicable, the host starts. In larger groups, you may proceed after several guests have been served and it is evident that service will be uneven; if a hosted function, the host should indicate to those already served to begin.

Whether eating American or Continental style, only one or two pieces of food are cut at a time for consumption. Food should be brought to the mouth, such that there is minimal bending of your body to meet the fork or spoon. In certain instances, foods such as asparagus (not juicy or covered with sauce), bacon (crisp), celery, chicken (informal meal) and sandwiches may be picked up with the fingers. However, if in doubt about whether to use your fingers, even when it is otherwise proper, always opt for using a utensil, particularly at a business meal, formal dinner or an official function. You should chew food with your mouth closed, and talk only when your mouth is not full. If an uncut loaf of bread is served, the host (if present) should cut several slices before it is passed on to guests. For bread and rolls, break off a small piece to be consumed and, holding it near the butter plate, butter that portion. Hot breads such as muffins and rolls are cut in half and may be entirely buttered before eating; toast should be buttered first, and then cut in half. All edible garnishes (such as cherries, orange slices, parsley, watercress) that are served with beverages and food may be eaten. Vegetables which are served in a side dish may be eaten with a fork directly from the dish or transferred with your fork or spoon to the dinner plate.

Remove troublesome food, bones or pits from your mouth with as little notice as possible, and place the item on your plate and cover it with a bit of food, if needed. If food gets lodged in your teeth, excuse yourself and dislodge it in the restroom or wait until the meal is completed; do not use a toothpick or your finger to dislodge food at the table (in contrast to etiquette in some Asian countries). Never lick your fingers after using your hands to eat; use your napkin. While eating, the hand/wrist not in use may be rested in your lap or on the table edge, but one's elbows should not be on the table. Cover your mouth with the napkin to burp, and then quietly say "Excuse me." If about to cough or sneeze, cover your mouth and nose with your handkerchief (if readily available) or napkin. Use only a handkerchief or tissue to blow your nose; if necessary, excuse yourself from the table. A woman may quickly check her make-up at the table, but neither women nor men should comb or otherwise touch their hair at the dining table. Small beverage spills may be removed from clothing or tablecloth by blotting with your napkin. Food spills may be removed with a clean piece of flatware, as well. For spills that require a damp cloth, excuse yourself and go the restroom.

Flatware that has been picked up and used should not be placed back on the table again. The principal utensils being used are placed on the main plate and, for example, spoons used for soup are placed in a shallow bowl or on the soup bowl under plate, and spoons used to stir coffee or iced tea are placed on the edge of the saucer. Note that any *unused* flatware should be left in place on the table and not put with the used utensils.

Before dessert is served, the table is cleared of serving dishes, dinnerware and condiments, and the table is crumbed (i.e., the bread crumbs are removed). At a business meal or formal dinner, diners should not hand plates to the server unless it is evident that a particular item on the table cannot be reached.

Occasionally, finger bowls are offered before or after dessert. Normally, the finger bowl with a doily underneath is placed on the dessert plate, with the dessert fork and spoon to each side of the bowl. Dip the fingers of each hand into the bowl and dry them with your napkin. Then, remove the dessert fork and spoon from the plate and place them to the left and right side of the plate, respectively. With both hands, move the finger bowl and doily to a position at the upper left of your place setting.

TOASTS

A toast is offered to honor individuals or institutions and imparts a special significance to an event. The host, a senior officer or official should make the first toast. This is typically done once the dessert has been served and wine or champagne glasses are filled. See the Chapter *Dining-In & Dining-Out* and the Section *Official Dinners & Receptions* for detailed information.

Restaurant Dining

Restaurant dining, when other than a routine lunch with colleagues, may be for the purpose of conducting business, marking an organization-related occasion, or may be primarily social in nature. Whatever the purpose, restaurant dining requires a familiarity with some protocol that is in addition to general table etiquette. This section should be reviewed along with the Sections *Table Settings* and *Table Manners*.

RESERVATIONS, ARRIVAL, SEATING

If you are hosting a lunch or dinner in a restaurant, you will be responsible for arrangements and coordination of the meal. Planning ahead, particularly for larger groups, is often essential to ensure a successful event. When making the reservation, specify any special requirements or service you want, such as requesting a more secluded or private area of the restaurant, or requesting a certain method for paying the bill. For very important occasions, visit the restaurant beforehand and confirm all arrangements, including, if applicable, where individuals are to sit. You should also consider providing the maître d' (head waiter) with a tip in advance of the function.

The host should be at the restaurant early enough to greet arriving guests. If the host or some guests have not arrived on time, the maître d' should be so informed by those present. They usually then have the option of staying at the restaurant's waiting area or proceeding to the table to wait for the others to arrive. Nothing on the dining table should be disturbed while waiting for others. If ten to fifteen minutes have elapsed and everyone is still not present, begin with any beverage/drink orders. If someone you know is seated elsewhere in the restaurant, avoid leaving the table, but merely nod in acknowledgement to the other person when eye contact is made.

As guests arrive at the table, the host should stand, greet and introduce them, as appropriate. As a courtesy, officers should also stand when very senior officers arrive at the table. The best seats, such as armchairs, seats which are away from busy aisles or the banquette (bench seat along a wall) should be given to senior officers/officials and visiting guests. If seating is prearranged, men and women should be dispersed around the table, such that there is no apparent segregation. At larger functions where there is an honored guest, he/she is seated to the right of the host.

ORDERING

The host should recommend a few menu items for which the restaurant is noted and suggest, if budget is not a concern, one or two more expensive main courses to signal to guests that they should feel free to order what they want. Otherwise, guests should select a moderately priced menu item (i.e., select neither the least nor most expensive item, because either might be a slight to the host). Items may be ordered à la carte, where each item is separately priced, or table d'hôte, a complete meal at a set price. Guests may ask the server/waiter about specialty dishes or for his/her recommendation. On the other hand, it is unwise at more official lunches or dinners to ask the waiter about a dish you should ordinarily know about or when you are unsure how to pronounce it. When the primary function of the meal is to conduct business, ease of consumption should also be kept in mind when selecting the main course. Each person should order for himself and be ready to answer the waiter's inquiries about selections and food preparation.

After all food orders are taken, the host should order wine, if it is desired. The wine order will be taken by the waiter or a wine steward (sommelier). The host who has little knowledge of wines should either ask the waiter/wine steward for his recommendation or ask a knowledgeable guest to make the selection. A good quality wine should be chosen, based on what most people have selected for their main course. White and red wines may both be ordered, although only a white wine or a red wine, carefully chosen, will often complement any combination of foods.

Conversing, Eating

Conversation should be limited to small talk until the waiter has taken everyone's order, including the wine order, and removed the menus; only then should business discussions commence. If the function is primarily a business meal, the host (if applicable) should initiate the business discussion. If the function is more social in nature, each guest has some responsibility to ensure that his neighbors at the table are included in conversation. For example, after conversing for a while with the person to his right, a diner should turn to the neighbor on his left and initiate a dialogue.

Eating should begin only after everyone has been served. However, if it is apparent that the service is unduly delayed and to wait would result in the meals already served becoming cold, those diners already served can begin eating, but should make a brief acknowledgement of the need to proceed. If there is a guest of honor, he should begin eating first, followed by the other guests and then the host. Absent an honored guest, the host should urge everyone to begin if there is hesitation.

In addition to the information contained in the Sections *Table Settings* and *Table Manners*, there are several things to note when eating in a restaurant. It is the host's responsibility to manage the table and call a waiter to the table when needed. Guests should keep complaints to a minimum and quietly convey any problems to the host or, at larger affairs or absent a host, to the waiter. Call the waiter to replace unclean or dropped utensils (do not wipe them off with your napkin) and to clean up spills on the floor.

When coffee cups are turned upside down on their saucers, turn them upright when coffee is being poured to receive coffee service. Empty unit-of-use condiment containers or packets should be put on an unused plate or, if unavailable, on or next to the butter plate or rim of the coffee cup saucer, as appropriate. Requesting a "doggie bag" at the end of a meal may be acceptable on certain social dining occasions where guests are well known to each other; it is inappropriate, however, when dining at a formal business or professional function. It is preferable that arrangements be made beforehand for the meal check to be received at a hosted function away from the table.

CHAPTER TEN

U.S. PUBLIC HEALTH SERVICE

There are seven uniformed services of the United States, each of which has certain characteristics that identify it as a unique service organization. The U.S. Public Health Service has a distinguished history of serving the public health needs of the Nation, and its reach now extends internationally. While acknowledging its 200-year heritage, the PHS is forging ahead in ways that will herald a new era in its history. This overview provides a description of the PHS organization, leadership, and the agencies and offices that comprise it, and highlights some important features of the PHS and its Commissioned Corps.

> MISSION
> ORGANIZATION
> OFFICE OF THE SURGEON GENERAL
> AGENCY ASSIGNMENTS
> REGULAR AND READY RESERVE CORPS
> U.S. PUBLIC HEALTH SERVICE HISTORY
> PUBLIC HEALTH SERVICE FLAG
> PUBLIC HEALTH SERVICE SEAL
> PHS COMMISSIONED CORPS SEAL
> PHS MARCH AND FANFARE
> PHS COIN

Mission

The mission of the Public Health Service Commissioned Corps is to
protect, promote, and advance the health and safety of our Nation.
The Commissioned Corps achieves this mission through:
- rapid and effective response to public health needs,
- leadership and excellence in public health practices, and,
- the advancement of public health science.

The PHS Commissioned Corps is comprised of highly trained health professionals who carry out health-related programs, prevent disease and injury, assure safe and effective drugs, deliver health services, and provide health expertise during national or international public health emergencies. These officers may be assigned to Federal, state or local agencies or international organizations. Currently, PHS officers serve within 25 agencies and operating divisions inclusive of 9 different U.S. Departments, and work in 800 locations worldwide. To accomplish its mission, the agencies/programs are designed to:

- Provide essential healthcare and related services to medically underserved, disadvantaged, and special needs populations.
- Prevent and control disease, identify and help correct health hazards in the environment, and promote healthy lifestyles for the Nation's citizens.
- Improve the Nation's mental health.
- Ensure that drugs and medical devices are safe and effective, food is safe and wholesome, cosmetics are harmless, and that electronic products do not expose users to dangerous amounts of radiation.
- Conduct and support biomedical, behavioral and health services research and communicate research results to health professionals and the public.
- Work with other nations and international agencies on global health problems and their solutions.

Organization

Department of Health and Human Services
The Department of Health and Human Services (HHS) is the principal executive level agency with the mission of protecting the health of Americans and providing essential human services. HHS employs Civil Service and Commissioned Corps officers to accomplish that mission, who are assigned to numerous agencies, including eleven Operating Divisions (OpDivs), ten Regional Offices and several Offices in addition to the Office of the Secretary. A major organizational program component of HHS is the Public Health Service, consisting of Offices and eight of the OpDivs, including, for example, the Centers for Disease Control and Prevention, Food and Drug Administration, Indian Health Service, and National Institutes of Health.

Office of the Assistant Secretary for Health
Among the HHS Offices is the Office of the Assistant Secretary for Health (OASH), which oversees fourteen core public health Offices, including the Office of the Surgeon General. The Assistant Secretary for Health is the principal advisor to the Secretary of Health and Human Services on public health and scientific issues. The Surgeon General reports to and advises the Assistant Secretary on public health matters relating to the health of Americans.

Office of the Surgeon General

The Office of the Surgeon General is led by the U.S. Surgeon General, who is appointed by the President with the advice and consent of the Senate for a four-year term of office. The Surgeon General serves as head of the USPHS Commissioned Corps and holds the rank of Vice Admiral. Many SGs have held the rank of Rear Admiral, however, mostly those whose terms of office were prior to 1965. David Satcher held the rank of a four-star admiral, due to his simultaneous service as Surgeon General and Assistant Secretary for Health from 1998 to 2002. The only SG to not have a uniformed service rank was John M. Woodworth, the first office holder, from 1871 to 1879.

The USPHS Commissioned Corps is a select cadre of 6,700 highly trained public health professionals in the following professional categories: dentist, dietitian, engineer, environmental health, health services, nurse, pharmacist, physician, scientist, therapist, and veterinarian. Officers are assigned to HHS and non-HHS agencies (e.g., PHS officers provide healthcare services to the U.S. Coast Guard). Officers may be deployed throughout the world and, in times of war, may be assigned to any of the armed forces, as necessary. Since its earliest days, the Corps has provided a centrally-administered, mobile and highly trained organization of health professionals who serve with distinction in a wide variety of clinical, research and public health leadership positions.

The immediate Office of the Surgeon General (OSG), under the direction of the Surgeon General, oversees the USPHS Commissioned Corps and provides support for the Surgeon General in the accomplishment of his/her duties. The OSG is comprised of four principal divisions to fulfill the OSG mission:

- **Division of Science and Communications**
  The division advises the SG on science and data pertaining to public health priorities, plans activities such as conferences and workshops, and prepares correspondence, speeches, authoritative statements and official reports.

- **Division of Commissioned Corps Personnel and Readiness**
  The division provides the day-to-day management of operations, personnel, recruitment, assignments, training, readiness, deployment, promotion, and retirement of commissioned officers. The division formulates policies and performance standards, proposes regulations, and works with OSG to facilitate operations and implement policies and programs. Organizationally, DCCPR has three Branches: the Recruitment Branch, Assignments and Career Management Branch, and, Ready Reserve Branch.

- **Division of the Civilian Volunteer Medical Reserve Corps**
  The division coordinates the Medical Reserve Corps (MRC), and supports and sustains a national network of 1,000 MRC units and 200,000 volunteers.

- **Division of Systems Integration**
  The division oversees information technology systems that serve the Commissioned Corps' personnel operations.

Deputy Surgeon General

The Deputy Surgeon General (DSG) has a critical role within the Office of the Surgeon General. The DSG is an active partner with the Surgeon General in the development of new policies, procedures, and programs, implementing initiatives, and advising the SG on operational and policy matters. He/she works closely with the Division of Commissioned Corps Personnel and Readiness and is responsible for overseeing the daily operations of the Commissioned Corps. The DSG also serves in the place of the SG, as needed.

Surgeon General Responsibilities

In carrying out his responsibilities, the Surgeon General reports to and advises the Assistant Secretary for Health (ASH), who is a principal advisor to the Secretary of Health and Human Services on public health and scientific issues. The Surgeon General is tasked with a myriad of responsibilities related to ensuring the health and welfare of the Nation. He commands the Commissioned Corps, including managing the Corps' personnel operations and force readiness. As the Nation's Doctor, the SG provides Americans with the best scientific information available on medical and public health issues; maintains ongoing communication with professional and scientific groups; represents the PHS at national and international public health and professional meetings; provides oversight of the Medical Reserve Corps program; and provides liaison with governmental and private organizations on matters pertaining to uniformed service and veterans affairs. Importantly, the Surgeon General chairs the National Prevention Council, which provides coordination and leadership among 20 executive departments with respect to prevention, wellness and health promotion activities. The Deputy Surgeon General serves as the principal assistant to the Surgeon General, and advises the SG on operational matters, including the development and implementation of initiatives, policies, programs, and priorities.

History of OSG
[See also *U.S. Public Health Service History*]

In 1798, Congress established the U.S. Marine Hospital Service – predecessor of today's U.S. Public Health Service – to provide health care to sick and injured merchant seamen. In 1870, the Marine Hospital Service was reorganized as a national hospital system with centralized administration under a medical officer, the Supervising Surgeon, who was later given the title of Surgeon General.

Dr. John Woodworth, appointed as the first Supervising Surgeon in 1871, established a cadre of medical personnel to administer the Marine Hospital System. On January 4, 1889, the Congress recognized this new personnel system by formally authorizing the Commissioned Corps along military lines to be a mobile force of professionals. Although initially composed only of physicians, the Corps' functional responsibilities broadened over the years to include a commensurate range of health professionals.

Prior to 1968, the Surgeon General was head of the Public Health Service, and all program, administrative, and financial management authorities flowed through the Surgeon General, who reported directly to the Secretary of Health, Education, and Welfare (predecessor of HHS). In 1968, pursuant to a reorganization plan issued by the President, the Secretary delegated line responsibility for the PHS to the Assistant Secretary for Health (ASH) and the SG became principal deputy with advisory responsibilities. In 1972, the SG again became advisor to the Secretary; in 1977 the positions of Assistant Secretary and SG were combined; and, in 1981, they were separated again. In 1987, the OSG was reestablished as an Office within the OASH. Concomitant with this action, the Surgeon General again became primarily responsible for management of the Commissioned Corps and an advisory role. With fewer administrative responsibilities and beginning in the 1980s with SG Koop, the Surgeons General have become more involved in national and global public health issues, and proactive as a trusted spokesperson in informing the public on health matters that affect the Nation.

The First Surgeon General

John Maynard Woodworth was born on August 15, 1837, in Big Flats, New York. He studied pharmacy at the University of Chicago and, in 1862, graduated from Rush Medical College. Upon graduation, Woodworth was appointed Assistant Surgeon in the Union Army, later promoted to Surgeon, and eventually became medical director of the Army of the Tennessee, serving under General Sherman. Following the Civil War, Dr. Woodworth became an anatomy professor at the Chicago Medical College, was Surgeon of the Soldier's home of Chicago and Sanitary Inspector of the Chicago Board of Health.

In 1871 John Woodworth was appointed the first Supervising Surgeon to administer the Marine Hospital Service (MHS), which was a network of hospitals that provided medical services to merchant seamen in American ports (see *PHS History,* below). Dr. Woodworth moved quickly to reform the system, laboring steadfastly and with resolve to remedy significant abuses and deficiencies within the Hospital Service, and adopting a military model for his medical staff. In 1872, Dr. Woodworth served as a founder of the American Public Health Association and, in 1873, in recognition of his outstanding leadership, his title was changed to Supervising Surgeon General. Dr. Woodworth envisioned a national approach to public health in service to the entire Nation. Among his many accomplishments were his meticulously written reports on the MHS that profoundly altered their operation, his close working relationship with State and local authorities, and the assignment of MHS medical officers to deal with smallpox, yellow fever, and other epidemic diseases.

In 1875, Woodworth's issuance of directives regarding quarantine and public health were the first action by the Federal government relating to quarantine since 1799. His national leadership and issuance of publications on cholera and yellow fever were instrumental in passage of the National Quarantine Act of 1878. The Act conferred quarantine authority on the MHS and authorized the publication of weekly abstracts of sanitary reports which were the predecessor of the journal *Public Health Reports*. The MHS moved into broadened spheres of public health activity, thereby setting the foundation for the Public Health Service. John Maynard Woodworth continued as Supervising Surgeon General until his death on March 14, 1879.

John Woodworth was a person of great capability, perseverance, resourcefulness, and achievement, who left an indelible mark on the advancement of public health. His legacy as military officer, academic, health care professional, national public health leader, and the first Surgeon General proved to be the standard for generations of US Public Health Service officers.

Surgeons General

Eighteen individuals have served as Surgeon General.

Surgeon General, 1871 – 2014

1st	John M. Woodworth, 1871 – 1879	11th	Jesse L. Steinfeld, 1969 – 1973
2nd	John B. Hamilton, 1879 – 1891	12th	Julius B. Richmond, 1977 – 1981
3rd	Walter Wyman, 1891 – 1911	13th	C. Everett Koop, 1982 – 1989
4th	Rupert Blue, 1912 – 1920	14th	Antonia C. Novello, 1990 – 1993
5th	Hugh S. Cumming, 1920 – 1936	15th	M. Joycelyn Elders, 1993 – 1994
6th	Thomas Parran, Jr., 1936 – 1948	16th	David Satcher, 1998 – 2002
7th	Leonard A. Scheele, 1948 – 1956	17th	Richard H. Carmona, 2002 – 2006
8th	Leroy E. Burney, 1956 – 1961	18th	Regina M. Benjamin, 2009 – 2013
9th	Luther L. Terry, 1961 – 1965	19th	
10th	William H. Stewart, 1965 – 1969		

Acting Surgeons General

The following individuals have served as Acting Surgeon General.

Acting Surgeon General, 1973 – 2014

*	S. Paul Ehrlich, 1973 – 1977	*	Kenneth P. Moritsugu, 2002
*	Edward Brandt, Jr., 1981 – 1982	*	Kenneth P. Moritsugu, 2006 – 2007
*	James O. Mason, 1989 – 1990	*	Steven K. Galson, 2007 – 2009
*	Robert A. Whitney, 1993	*	Donald L. Weaver, 2009
*	Audrey F. Manley, 1995 – 1997	*	Boris D. Lushniak, 2013 – Present
*	J. Jarrett Clinton, 1997 – 1998		

Deputy Surgeons General
The following individuals have served as Deputy Surgeon General.

Deputy Surgeon General, 1944 – 2014

Warren F. Draper, 1944 – 1946	John C. Greene, 1978 – 1981
James A. Crabtree, 1946 – 1948	Faye G. Abdellah, 1981 – 1989
W. Palmer Dearing, 1948 – 1957	O. Marie Henry, 1990 – 1992
John D. Porterfield, 1957 – 1962	Robert A. Whitney, 1992 – 1993
David Price, 1962 – 1965	Audrey F. Manley, 1994 – 1997
Leo Gehrig, 1965 – 1968	Kenneth P. Moritsugu, 1998 – 2007
S. Paul Ehrlich, 1968 – 1977	Boris D. Lushniak, 2010 – Present

Agency Assignments

The HHS/USPHS Commissioned Corps, unlike other uniformed service personnel systems in the Department of Defense, does not directly employ all officers, with the exception of those who administer the commissioned personnel program. PHS officers are assigned to and employed by individual agencies, offices and programs of HHS and other non-HHS organizations. The following is a brief description of agencies, operating divisions (OpDivs) and programs where commissioned officers may serve.

HHS Agencies and Offices
in which PHS Officers Serve
[Often referred to as Operating Divisions]

Agency for Healthcare Research and Quality (AHRQ)
> AHRQ supports research designed to improve the outcomes and quality of health care, reduce its costs, address patient safety and medical errors, and broaden access to effective services. The research sponsored and conducted by AHRQ provides needed information about health care.

Agency for Toxic Substances and Disease Registry (ATSDR)
> ATSDR's mission is to prevent exposure and adverse human health effects and diminished quality of life associated with exposure to hazardous substances from waste sites, unplanned releases, and other sources of pollution present in the environment.

Centers for Disease Control and Prevention (CDC)
> CDC's mission is to promote health and quality of life by preventing and controlling disease, injury, and disability. CDC works with national and international partners to monitor health, detect and investigate health problems, conduct research to enhance prevention, develop and advocate

sound public health policies, implement prevention strategies, promote healthy behaviors, foster safe and healthful environments, and provide leadership and training. CDC also has a major role in protecting the public from biological and chemical terrorism.

Centers for Medicare and Medicaid Services (CMS)

CMS administers the Medicare and Medicaid programs, which provide health care to America's aged and indigent populations. CMS also administers the State Children's Health Insurance Program; the Medicare Prescription Drug, Improvement, and Modernization Act; and, the Health Insurance Portability and Accountability Act. In addition, it performs a number of quality-focused activities, including regulation of laboratory testing, quality-of-care improvement, oversight of the survey and certification of nursing homes and continuing care providers (home health agencies, intermediate care facilities for mentally retarded, and hospitals).

Food and Drug Administration (FDA)

FDA, one of the Nation's oldest consumer protection agencies, ensures the safety of foods and cosmetics and the safety and efficacy of pharmaceuticals, biological products, and medical devices. Its employees monitor the manufacture, import, transport, storage, and sale of about $1 trillion worth of products each year.

Health Resources and Services Administration (HRSA)

HRSA directs national health programs that improve the Nation's health by assuring equitable access to comprehensive, quality health care for all. It works to improve and extend life for people living with HIV/AIDS, provide primary health care to medically underserved people, serve women and children through State programs, and train a health workforce to work in underserved communities.

Indian Health Service (IHS)

IHS is the principal Federal health care advocate and provider for American Indians and Alaska Natives who belong to more than 550 Federally recognized tribes in 35 States. It provides comprehensive health care services, including preventive, curative, rehabilitative and environmental.

National Institutes of Health (NIH)

NIH, composed of 27 Institutes and Centers, is one of the world's foremost medical research centers, providing leadership and financial support to researchers throughout the Nation and the world. Its mission is to help lead the way toward important medical discoveries that improve health and save lives. NIH scientists investigate ways to prevent disease, as well as the causes, treatments, and cures for common and rare diseases.

Office of the Assistant Secretary for Health (OASH)
The OASH is under the direction of the Assistant Secretary of Health, who serves as the senior advisor on public health and science issues to the Secretary of HHS. The office serves as the focal point of leadership and coordination in public health and science across HHS; provides direction to program offices within OASH; and provides advice and counsel to the Secretary on public health and science issues.

Office of the Assistant Secretary for Preparedness and Response (ASPR)
The Office of ASPR serves as the HHS Secretary's principal advisory staff on matters related to bioterrorism and other public health emergencies. ASPR coordinates interagency activities among HHS, other Federal departments and agencies, and State and local officials responsible for emergency preparedness and the protection of the civilian population.

Office of the Secretary (OS)
The Department of Health and Human Services is the Nation's principal agency for protecting the health of all Americans and providing essential human services. The department includes more than 300 major programs covering a wide spectrum of health and human welfare activities. OS oversees program missions and accomplishments, and coordinates a budget that accounts for almost one-fourth of all Federal expenditures.

Program Support Center (PSC)
The PSC provides government support products and services on a fee-for-service basis to customers throughout HHS and approximately thirteen other executive departments and eighteen independent Federal agencies.

Substance Abuse and Mental Health Services Administration (SAMHSA)
SAMHSA works to improve the quality and availability of prevention, treatment, and rehabilitative services in order to reduce illness, disability, death, and costs resulting from substance abuse and mental illness.

Non-HHS Agencies and Programs
in which PHS Officers Serve

District of Columbia Commission on Mental Health Services (CMHS)
The CMHS works toward establishing a community-based system of care for individuals with mental health problems in Washington D.C.

Environmental Protection Agency (EPA)
EPA implements the Federal laws designed to promote public health by protecting the Nation's air, water, and soil from harmful pollution through proper integration of a variety of research, monitoring, standard setting, and enforcement activities. EPA supports research and anti-pollution activities of State and local governments, private and public groups, individuals, and educational institutions. EPA also monitors operations of Federal agencies with respect to their impact on the environment.

Federal Bureau of Prisons (BOP)
The mission of BOP, as part of the Department of Justice, is to protect society by confining offenders in the controlled environments of prisons and community-based facilities that are safe, humane, appropriately secure, and that provide work and other self-improvement opportunities to assist offenders in becoming law-abiding citizens.

National Oceanic and Atmospheric Administration (NOAA)
NOAA, organizationally within the Department of Commerce, is responsible for conducting research and gathering data about the global oceans, atmosphere and space. NOAA predicts changes in the earth's environment, forecasts weather patterns, and warns of dangerous weather; charts the seas and skies; and, guides the use and protection of ocean and coastal resources. PHS officers provide health care services to NOAA active duty members, dependents and retirees.

National Park Service (NPS)
The NPS was established to preserve the natural and cultural resources and values of the national parks for this and future generations. It administers more than 378 national parks, monuments, historic sites, and other areas covering almost 80 million acres.

U.S. Department of Agriculture (USDA)
The USDA supports the production of agriculture by ensuring a safe, affordable, nutritious and accessible food supply; caring for agricultural, forest, and rangelands; supporting development of rural communities; providing economic opportunities for farm and rural residents; expanding global markets for agricultural and forest products and services; and, working to reduce hunger in the U.S. and throughout the world.

U.S. Department of Defense (DOD)
The mission of the DOD is to provide the military forces needed to deter war and protect the security of the Nation. This is accomplished through the coordinated efforts of the defense agencies and military services. PHS officers are detailed to DOD facilities to support a range of medical and mental health services, as well as administrative functions.

U.S. Department of Homeland Security (DHS)
Established in 2002, DHS is charged with mobilizing and organizing a unified national effort to secure America against terrorist attacks and to protect against and respond to threats and hazards to our Nation. In carrying out this mission, DHS works to ensure safe and secure borders, welcome lawful immigrants and visitors, and promote the free flow of commerce. PHS officers work throughout DHS agencies, such as the Federal Emergency Management Agency, Customs and Border Protection, and the U.S. Coast Guard where they provide medical and dental care to Coast Guard active duty members, dependents and retirees.

U.S. Marshals Service (USMS)
> USMS, an agency of the U.S. Department of Justice (DOJ), protects the Federal courts and ensures the effective operation of the judicial system; provides for the security, health, and safety of government witnesses and their immediate dependents; and, housing and transporting prisoners in Federal custody. PHS officers provide needed medical support services.

Policy Advisory Council

See the *Surgeon General's Policy Advisory Council (SGPAC)* in the Chapter, *Special Duty*.

Regular and Ready Reserve Corps

Regular Corps
The Patient Protection and Affordable Care Act, commonly referred to as the Affordable Care Act (ACA) and enacted in March 23, 2010, effected certain changes to the USPHS, as follows: eliminated the cap of 2,800 PHS Regular Corps officers; deemed PHS Reserve Corps officers serving on active duty at the time of enactment to be officers of the Regular Corps; and, eliminated the Reserve Corps and established a Ready Reserve Corps. As a result, newly appointed PHS officers are now commissioned for extended active duty in the Regular Corps.

Ready Reserve Corps
The purpose of the Ready Reserve Corps is to have additional Commissioned Corps personnel available on short notice to assist Regular Corps personnel to meet both routine public health and emergency response missions. Ready Reserve members perform duties for assigned periods of time, as opposed to full time Regular Corps members. Joining the Ready Reserve Corps is voluntary; however, members of the Ready Reserve Corps join knowing that they can be called at any time to serve in times of national need.

The Ready Reserve Corps officers will participate in routine training; be available and ready for calls to active duty during national emergencies and public health crises, or to backfill critical positions left vacant during deployment of Regular Corps members; or be available for service assignments in isolated, hardship and medically underserved communities.

Presently, HHS is still in the process of reviewing that provision of the legislation which created the Ready Reserve Corps to determine how it will be implemented and function operationally.

U.S. Public Health Service History

The Nineteenth Century

The origins of the United States Public Health Service (PHS) began in 1798, when President John Adams signed into law the *Act for the Relief of Sick and Disabled Seamen*, which provided for the care and relief of sick and injured merchant seamen that was financed through deductions from the wages of seamen. A year later, Congress extended the *Act* to cover U.S. Naval personnel. The earliest marine hospitals were located along the East Coast, first in Boston, and later along inland waterways, the Great Lakes and the Gulf and Pacific Coasts. This loose network of marine hospitals was called the Marine Hospital Service (MHS). However, the hospitals were poorly organized, hospital funding was inadequate, and political rather than medical reasons often influenced the choice of hospital sites. Union and Confederate forces occupied the hospitals during the Civil War, and only 8 of 27 hospitals were operational thereafter. In 1869, a study of the marine hospitals led to passage of reform legislation the following year. The 1870 reorganization led to a centrally controlled national agency with Headquarters in Washington, DC.

The position of Supervising Surgeon (later Surgeon General) was created to administer the Service, and John Maynard Woodworth was appointed as the first incumbent in 1871. He quickly reformed the system and adopted a military model for his medical staff, instituting examinations for applicants and putting his physicians in uniforms. Woodworth created a cadre of career service physicians who could be assigned as needed to the various marine hospitals. The uniformed services component of the Marine Hospital Service was formalized as the Commissioned Corps when, in 1889, President Grover Cleveland signed *An Act to Regulate Appointments in the Marine Hospital Service of the United States*. The Corps was established along military lines to be a mobile force of professionals subject to reassignment to meet the needs of the Service. Originally composed only of physicians, the functional responsibilities of the PHS and Corps broadened during the twentieth century, and the Corps expanded to include dentists, sanitarians, engineers, pharmacists, nurses, sanitarians, scientists, and other health professionals.

The scope of activities of the Marine Hospital Service began to expand beyond the provision of health care to merchant seamen. A number of infectious disease epidemics occurred throughout the 19th century, including a significant yellow fever epidemic in 1877. Responsibility for quarantine was originally a function of the states, but the *National Quarantine Act of 1878* conferred quarantine authority on the Marine Hospital Service. Over the course of the next half a century, the Marine Hospital Service increasingly took over quarantine functions from state authorities. In 1887, the Service established a bacteriological laboratory, called the Hygienic Laboratory, at the marine hospital on Staten Island, New York. In 1891, it moved to Washington, DC, becoming the predecessor of the National Institutes of Health.

Immigration increased dramatically in the late 19th century, and the Federal government also took over from the states responsibility for the processing of immigrants. Pursuant to the *Immigration Act of 1891*, the Marine Hospital Service was assigned the responsibility for the medical inspection of arriving immigrants at sites such as Ellis Island in New York. Commissioned officers played a major role in fulfilling the service's commitment to prevent disease from entering the country.

The Twentieth Century
The widening responsibilities of the Service and need for better consolidation and coordination led to passage of an *Act* in 1902 that changed the name of the MHS to the Public Health and Marine Hospital Service, and was shortened in 1912 to the Public Health Service. During World War II, many PHS officers were detailed to the military, including over 600 who served with the Coast Guard. Concomitant with these broadened responsibilities were major reorganizations and creation of new agencies where PHS commissioned officers served, and realignment of authorities relating to the position of Surgeon General (see *History of OSG*). In 1953, the Federal Security Agency, where the Public Health Service had been organizationally located since 1939, was elevated to Cabinet level status and renamed the Department of Health, Education, and Welfare; and, in 1980 it was renamed the Department of Health and Human Services (HHS). The PHS has continued to broaden its public health activities and, as the century progressed, the duties and functions of the PHS have encompassed the control and prevention of communicable disease, biomedical research, regulation of food and drugs, mental health and drug abuse, international health, and provision of health care to underserved groups, including individuals suffering from leprosy, American Indians and Alaska natives, those in federal prisons, and immigrants to the U.S. There have been numerous world-class biomedical achievements by the Public Health Service and PHS commissioned officers.

Reports of the Surgeon General. The more recognized accomplishments of the Service often relate to a Surgeon General's initiatives to inform the public about health and medical issues at the national level. The issuance of science-based documents regarding major public health problems, called Reports of the Surgeon General and Calls to Action, is one method. Notable reports include the landmark *Surgeon General's Report on Smoking and Health*, issued by Surgeon General Terry in 1964, which affirmed that smoking cigarettes causes lung cancer. Surgeon General Richmond is best known for implementing quantitative health goals for the next decade by issuing the first "Healthy People" Report in 1979 as *Healthy People: The Surgeon General's Report on Health Promotion and Disease Prevention*. Surgeon General Koop's tenure from 1982-89 was highlighted by his public health stance on AIDS, release of the Surgeon General's Report on *Acquired Immune Deficiency Syndrome*, and the 1988 mailing of a brochure entitled *Understanding AIDS* to every household in the U.S.

Revitalization. In 1987, Surgeon General Koop launched a major effort to revitalize the Corps, with the intent of restoring the Commissioned Corps to its traditional leadership role. Actions were taken to enhance all aspects of Corps management, including recruitment, assignment, career development and communication. Career tracks were prepared for the eleven professional categories within the Corps to enhance opportunities for professional growth. Efforts were also made to ensure that agencies with PHS officers are actively involved in the formulation and review of policies and procedures related to administration of the Corps.

The Twenty-First Century

Transformation. Beginning in 2002 and first announced in July 2003, the Commissioned Corps began conceptualizing a new initiative known as the transformation of the Corps under Surgeon General Carmona, a process that spanned nearly ten years. The transformation plan was publicly announced in January 2006, with the primary intent being to develop the Corps as an essential national resource to meet urgent public health challenges, participate with other uniformed services on humanitarian missions abroad, and to provide a force management structure in billeting and assignments. The Corps is deployed as part of ESF-8 in the national emergency response framework, and officers can also be individually deployed for various needs to other federal agencies, states, local governments, or to aid foreign governments. Officers are deployed upon the recommendation of the Surgeon General and concurrence of the Assistant Secretary for Health.

Patient Protection and Affordable Care Act. The Patient Protection and Affordable Care Act, commonly referred to as the Affordable Care Act (ACA) and enacted March 23, 2010, effected some changes to the USPHS, as follows: eliminated the cap of 2,800 Regular Corps officers; deemed all Reserve Corps officers serving on active duty at the time of enactment to be officers of the Regular Corps; and, eliminated the Reserve Corps and established a Ready Reserve Corps. The ACA also created the National Prevention Council (NPC) to develop the National Prevention Strategy. Comprised of 20 federal departments, agencies and offices, it is chaired by the Surgeon General.

Global Public Health. Public health is a fundamental component of national security, as noted in the President's National Security Strategy that "The United States has a moral and strategic interest in promoting global health." In response, the armed services have all formed public health commands, and they turn to the USPHS Commissioned Corps for expertise as a public health force multiplier. As it embarks upon this new century, the PHS with the Commissioned Corps continues to fulfill its mission of protecting and advancing public health nationally and globally. It has grown from a small group of marine hospitals to the largest public health program in the world.

Public Health Service Flag

The PHS flag has a yellow background (gold hue) with a blue PHS seal centered on the Flag. The use of a yellow flag to denote quarantine dates back to the eighteenth century, and it appears that the PHS flag evolved from the yellow quarantine flag used by the Service on quarantine vessels and stations. By the early twentieth century, the PHS had added its seal to the traditional yellow flag, with the blue color representing the origins of the PHS in maritime activities. A version of that flag came to be used in connection with PHS activities. By the late 1960s, specifications for the flag were formally established, with the diameter of the PHS seal being one-half the height of the flag.

Public Health Service Seal

The PHS seal was originally designed by John Maynard Woodworth, who was appointed in 1871 as the first Supervising Surgeon (title was later changed to Surgeon General) of the Marine Hospital Service. The seal features a caduceus crossed with a fouled anchor, and it originally carried the words "U.S. Marine Hospital Service" with the dates 1798-1871. The 1798 date refers to the year of passage of the Act for the Relief of Sick and Disabled Seamen, which set up the marine hospital system that evolved into the PHS. Today's seal is similar, except that it carries the words "U.S. Public Health Service" and only one date, 1798. The fouled anchor signifies a seaman in distress or a sick seaman. Although the caduceus is often used as a symbol of medicine, the particular symbolic form used by Woodworth is more often associated with the god Mercury to represent trade or commerce, and it is surmised that this was used due to the Service's relationship with merchant seamen and the maritime industry.

PHS Commissioned Corps Seal

The PHS Commissioned Corps seal features the PHS service crest, and carries the words "USPHS Commissioned Corps" with the date 1889. The 1889 date is the year of passage of the *Act to Regulate Appointments in the Marine Hospital Service of the United States,* which formalized the Corps.

Public Health Service March and Fanfare

The *Public Health Service March* was composed by Senior Musician George King III, U.S. Coast Guard, who conveyed the copyright to the PHS Surgeon General in 1978. On the occasion of the PHS Corps Centennial in 1989, Senior Musician King, upon request, also composed the *Centennial Fanfare – Anchor and Caduceus*. The *PHS March* and the *Centennial Fanfare* represent the official music of the Public Health Service. The PHS March lyrics are as follows.

The mission of our Service is known the world around,
In research and in treatment no equal can be found.
In the silent war against disease no truce is ever seen,
We serve on the land and the sea for humanity,
The Public Health Service Team!

Public Health Service Coin

The uniformed service coin is used by service personnel as a form of recognition. The coin, also known as a *challenge* or *recognition coin,* is unique to a member's unit or uniformed service – it carries a likeness of the unit/service crest or insignia and may include its motto. The coin engenders an identity with, and camaraderie within one's own organization and among all service members who have served the Nation with distinction. PHS officers carry the coin to "show their colors," and are also used as appreciation gifts and mementos for presentation to supporters of the Corps. The Public Health Service coin was developed by the District of Columbia Branch, Commissioned Officers Association. The PHS coin is approximately 1½ inches in diameter. One side has a 4-color enamel surface displaying the PHS seal and the other side displays the PHS Commissioned Corps seal. The coin is finely detailed, and the face, borders and edges are bright gold finish.

There are various theories about how the coin evolved to become a symbol of military recognition. By most accounts, the tradition began during World War I when an American pilot ordered medallions struck that bore his squadron's insignia, which he presented to fellow pilots. He subsequently needed to establish his identify after escaping German capture, and then being mistaken by the French as a German saboteur – his only identification was his medallion, the insignia of which was recognized by a French guard. Pilots began to carry a recognition coin at all times and would challenge one another to produce the coin, and so came about the tradition of a coin check. The challenger holds his/her coin in the air, announcing "coin check" and/or drops the coin on a table, and those challenged must show their own coin. By custom, those not having a coin are obliged to buy the challenger a drink.

CHAPTER ELEVEN

UNIFORMED SERVICE ORGANIZATIONS

There are seven uniformed services of the United States: the Public Health Service, National Oceanic and Atmospheric Administration, Air Force, Army, Coast Guard, Marine Corps, and Navy. The last five services are considered the armed forces/services. All uniformed services have the common objective of providing security to the United States, and all follow similar conventions. Yet, each service has characteristics that identify it as a unique service organization. The following information provides an overview of each service. All uniformed services have a proud record of service to the Nation, and readers are encouraged to learn more about them. The following information is derived from Department of Defense and uniformed service publications.

DEPARTMENT OF DEFENSE

AIR FORCE

ARMY

COAST GUARD

MARINE CORPS

NAVY

NATIONAL OCEANIC & ATMOSPHERIC

ADMINISTRATION CORPS

Department of Defense

The Armed Forces are the military forces of the U.S., consisting of the Air Force, Army, Coast Guard, Marine Corps, and Navy. The President of the United States is the Commander in Chief of all uniformed services. The President is advised by the Secretary of Defense, Joint Chiefs of Staff (JCS), and the National Security Council with regard to national security. The Joint Chiefs of Staff consist of the Chairman, the Vice Chairman, top military officers of each service, to include the Chief of Staff of the Army, the Chief of Naval Operations, the Chief of Staff of the Air Force, the Commandant of the

Marine Corps, and the Chief of the National Guard Bureau (note that the Commandant of the Coast Guard is not a member of the JCS).

History

The Army, Navy, and Marine Corps were established in 1775, in concurrence with the American Revolution. The precursor to what is now the Department of Defense was the War Department, which was established in 1789. A year later, in 1790, the Coast Guard (now part of Homeland Security) was formed, followed by the founding of the Department of the Navy in 1798. The decision to unify the different services under one Department led to the creation of the National Military Establishment in 1947 to replace the War Department, which converted to the Department of the Army. That same year, the U.S. Air Force was established followed by the founding of the Department of the Air Force. The three military branches, Army, Navy, and Air Force, were placed under the direct control of the new Secretary of Defense. In 1949, an amendment to the National Security Act further consolidated the national defense structure by withdrawing Cabinet-level status from the three Service secretaries. The National Military Establishment was then renamed the Department of Defense.

Mission

The mission of the Department of Defense is to provide the military forces needed to deter war and to protect the security of the Nation.

Operational Structure

The Department of Defense (DOD) is composed of the following: Office of the Secretary of Defense; Joint Chiefs of Staff; three Military Departments (Army, Air Force, Navy [includes Marine Corps]); Office of the Inspector General; 17 Defense Agencies (e.g., Defense Intelligence Agency); ten DOD Field Activities (e.g., DOD Education Activity); the National Guard Bureau; and, nine Combatant Commands.

The individual services are operationally subordinate to their **Military Departments**, each of which is directed by a civilian Secretary appointed by the President. The departments have a senior uniformed officer who commands their respective service – the Army Chief of Staff, Air Force Chief of Staff, Chief of Naval Operations, and Commandant of the Marine Corps – and who work with their department's Secretary to implement the DOD mission. The Secretaries and Service Chiefs do not have operational command authority over U.S. troops; rather, the departments are tasked with recruitment, training, provision of equipment, and administration of their forces.

The operational control and command of military forces are the responsibility of the nine **Unified Combatant Commands**, which are composed of two or more of the armed services. The combatant commands are governed by a Unified Command Plan, which details the Command's mission, geographical Area of Responsibility or Functional Responsibility, and force structure.

During military operations, the command chain is the President to the Secretary of Defense and, in turn, to the combatant commanders of the Combatant Commands. Following are the unified commands with their principal Areas of Responsibility (AR) or Functional Responsibility (FR).

Military Unified Combatant Commands

U.S. AFRICA COMMAND (AFRICOM), *AR – Africa*
    HQ Location: Stuttgart-Moehringen, Germany

U.S. CENTRAL COMMAND (CENTCOM), *AR – Middle East Region*
    HQ Location: MacDill AFB, Florida

U.S. EUROPEAN COMMAND (EUCOM), *AR – Greenland, Europe, Russia*
    HQ Location: Stuttgart, Germany

U.S. NORTHERN COMMAND (NORTHCOM), *AR – U.S., Canada, Mexico*
    HQ Location: Peterson AFB, Colorado

U.S. PACIFIC COMMAND (PACOM), *AR – Australia, China, India, Korea*
    HQ Location: Honolulu, Hawaii

U.S. SOUTHERN COMMAND (SOUTHCOM), *AR – Central and South America*
    HQ Location: Miami, Florida

U.S. SPECIAL OPERATIONS COMMAND (SOCOM), *FR – Special Operations*
    HQ Location: MacDill AFB, Florida

U.S. STRATEGIC COMMAND (STRATCOM), *FR – Coordinates Strategic Assets*
    HQ Location: Offutt AFB, Nebraska

U.S. TRANSPORTATION COMMAND (TRANSCOM), *FR – Global Transportation*
    HQ Location: Scott AFB, Illinois

Personnel
Presently, the uniformed services are an all-volunteer force, but with Congressional approval, males can be conscripted through the Selective Service. The military services have a combined strength of about 1.4 million active duty personnel and 1.1 million Reserve and National Guard personnel.

U.S. Air Force

History
The Air Force is the youngest of the armed forces, having been formally established in 1947. Its origins began in 1907 as the Aeronautical Division of the U.S. Army Signal Corps. The progress of American aviation was slow, however, with Congress voting an appropriation for the first time in 1911 and authorizing creation of the Army Aviation Section of the Signal Corps in 1914. The name changed to the Air Service in 1918 and then to the Army Air Corps in 1926, which became a subordinate element of the Army Air Forces in 1941 and continued as a combat arm of the Army until 1947. In 1947, President

Truman signed the National Security Act which provided for a new defense organization, DOD, and a separate Department of the Air Force. The important role of military aviation was proven during its use in World Wars I and II. The Air Force's combat role advanced from tactical support of ground forces to include strategic bombing and maintenance of U.S. nuclear forces.

Mission
The mission of the U.S. Air Force is to fly, fight and win ... in air, space, and cyberspace.

Organization
The Department of the Air Force is responsible for conducting military operations in air and space. It is administered by a civilian Secretary appointed by the President, and it is supervised by a military Chief of Staff appointed by the President with the consent of the Senate for a four-year term. The Secretary and Chief of Staff together direct the Air Force mission.

The Secretary of the Air Force is responsible for the conduct of all affairs of the Air Force, including administration, training, operations, logistical support and maintenance, personnel welfare, and research and development. The Chief of Staff of the Air Force presides over the Air Staff, transmits plans and recommendations to the Secretary and acts as the Secretary's agent in carrying them out. The Chief of Staff is responsible for the preparedness of its forces for military operations and supervises the administration of Air Force personnel assignments. The Chief of Staff also is a member of the Joint Chiefs of Staff.

The Air Force brings four distinct contributions to the military portfolio: air and space control; global intelligence, surveillance and reconnaissance; global mobility; and, global strike capability. Ten major Air Force commands, field operating agencies, and direct reporting units constitute the field organization that carries out the Air Force mission. In addition, there are two Reserve components, the Air Force Reserve, which is also a major command, and the Air National Guard. Major commands are organized on a functional basis in the United States and a geographic basis overseas. In descending order, elements of major commands include numbered air forces, wings (four or more squadrons), groups, squadrons, and flights. Air Combat Command (ACC) is the primary force provider of combat airpower to America's warfighting commands. Air Force combat forces are assigned, as directed by the Secretary of Defense, to the Unified Combatant Commands. ACC numbered air forces provide the air component to U.S. Central, Southern and Northern Commands, with Headquarters ACC serving as the air component to Joint Forces Commands. ACC also augments forces to U.S. European, Pacific and Strategic Command.

The Air Force is further divided into ten Aerospace Expeditionary Forces (AEFs), with each force composed of about the same air and space capability and approximately 175 aircraft, support equipment, and 15,000 personnel. Each AEF maintains readiness for immediate deployment for 90 days every 15 months, and two of the ten AEFs are on call at any one time. This approach allows the Air Force to better manage its resources in responding to world-wide contingencies.

Personnel

The current personnel strength of the Air Force is about 500,000 personnel: 330,000 active duty members, plus two Reserve components – the Air Force Reserve with about 70,000 members, and the Air National Guard with about 100,000 personnel.

U.S. Army

History

The Army is the oldest U.S. military service, with origins in the Continental Army which was created on June 14, 1775 at the outset of the Revolutionary War. Although disbanded after the war, the Regular Army was subsequently formed in 1791 and renamed the United States Army in 1796. The War of 1812 and the Mexican–American War (1846-1848) preceded the American Civil War (1861–1865), during which members of the Army were split between the Union Army and Confederate forces. In 1941, the "Army of the United States" was founded to fight World War II. Currently, the Army is comprised of the Regular Army, the Army Reserve, and the Army National Guard. National Guard units trace their lineage to the 1600s, when three colonial militia units were formed in Massachusetts. The Militia Act of 1903 and a 1933 amendment to the National Defense Act of 1916 created the Army National Guard of the U.S., whereby National Guardsmen are members of both their State National Guard (or militia) and, when federalized, the National Guard of the U.S.

Mission

The mission of the U.S. Army is to fight and win our Nation's wars by providing prompt, sustained land dominance across the full range of military operations and spectrum of conflict in support of combatant commanders.

Organization

The Department of the Army is responsible for conducting military operations on land. It is administered by a civilian Secretary appointed by the President, and it is supervised by a military Chief of Staff appointed by the President with the consent of the Senate for a four year term. The Secretary and Chief of Staff together direct the Army mission. The Secretary of the Army and Chief of Staff have responsibilities very similar to those of their counterparts in the Air Force and Navy, recruiting and administering Army personnel and providing trained forces to the Combatant Commands for use in military operations as directed by the Secretary of Defense. The Chief of Staff also serves as a member of the Joint Chiefs of Staff.

The army conducts both institutional and operational missions. There are three institutional Army Commands that provide the infrastructure necessary to recruit, train, equip and deploy Army forces: the U.S. Army Forces Command; Training and Doctrine Command; and, Materiel Command. The operational Army consists of numbered armies, corps, divisions, brigades, and battalions that conduct full spectrum operations around the world. They function in concert with the Unified Combatant Commands and include: the U.S. Army Africa Command; Central Command; Europe Command; North Command; Pacific Command; South Command; Special Operations Command; Military Surface Deployment and Distribution Command; and, Space and Missile Defense Command/Army Strategic Command. The Army's organizational force structure is generally as follows:

- Corps, 20,000 to 45,000 soldiers, with two to five divisions
- Division, 10,000 to 15,000 soldiers, usually consisting of three brigades
- Brigade, 3,000 to 5,000 soldiers, with two to five combat battalions
- Battalion, 300 to 1,000 soldiers, with four to six companies
- Company, 62 to 190 soldiers, with three to five platoons
- Platoon, 16 to 44 soldiers, with two to four squads
- Squad, nine or 10 soldiers.

Currently, the U.S. Army is structured around the Brigade Combat Team (BCT) as the basic deployable unit, which includes the support units needed to sustain its operations. Current plans are to reduce the number of BCTs from 45 to 33 by 2017. Three brigades include the Infantry BCT (4,400 soldiers, light infantry, air assault, or airborne), Stryker BCT (mechanized infantry force), and Armored BCT (armored force).

Personnel

The U.S. Army is comprised of the Regular Army, with over 500,000 active duty personnel, and two Reserve components – the Army Reserve with about 200,000 personnel, and, the individual state-based Army National Guard with about 350,000 personnel. The President or Secretary of Defense can activate state National Guard units into Federal military service, when needed.

U.S. Coast Guard

History

The Coast Guard traces its history back to August 4, 1790 when the first Congress authorized the construction of ten vessels to enforce tariff and trade laws, prevent smuggling, and protect the collection of the Federal revenue. Known variously as the Revenue Marine and the Revenue Cutter Service, the Coast Guard greatly expanded in size and responsibilities, to include humanitarian duties and law enforcement functions.

The Coast Guard was formed in 1915 under an act of Congress when the Revenue Cutter Service was merged with the Life-Saving Service. The new organization operated under the direction of the Department of the Treasury during peace time, and as part of the Navy in wartime.

The Lighthouse Service was transferred to the Coast Guard in 1939. Later, in 1946, Congress transferred the Bureau of Marine Inspection and Navigation to the Coast Guard, thereby placing merchant marine licensing and merchant vessel safety under its purview. In 1967, the CG was transferred to the Department of Transportation and, in 2003, it was again transferred to the Department of Homeland Security, pursuant to the *Homeland Security Act*.

Mission
The mission of the Coast Guard is to protect the maritime economy and the environment, defend our maritime borders, and save those in peril.

Organization
The Coast Guard (CG) is a branch of the armed forces that has a maritime law enforcement mission (with jurisdiction in both domestic and international waters) and a federal regulatory mission. It is responsible for protecting the Nation's interests in its ports and waterways, along its coastlines and in international waters. Its responsibilities can be broadly categorized as ensuring maritime safety, enforcing maritime security, protecting natural resources, and national defense. The Coast Guard can be transferred from the Department of Homeland Security to the Department of the Navy upon direction of the President, or by the U.S. Congress in time of war.

The Coast Guard resides organizationally within the Department of Homeland Security. A Coast Guard Commandant at headquarters in Washington, D.C. oversees all operations and supervises two major command areas: CG Atlantic Area (LANTAREA), headquartered in Portsmouth, Virginia, and the Pacific Area (PACAREA), headquartered in Alameda, California. These regional command forces provide maritime safety, security, and stewardship. The two command areas are divided into nine geographic districts for specific regions of the Nation. However, their Areas of Responsibility are international in scope, with LANTAREA also covering Africa, Europe and the Middle East, and PACAREA covering Asia, the Arctic and Antarctica.

The Coast Guard Auxiliary was authorized by act of Congress in 1939, and is comprised of civilian volunteers who assist the CG in performing any function, duty, role, mission or operation. They are probably best known for educating the public through boating safety classes.

Personnel
Current personnel strength is about 43,000 active duty members and 8,000 personnel in the Coast Guard Reserve. Approximately 32,000 civilian volunteers comprise the Coast Guard Auxiliary.

U.S. Marine Corps

History

The Marine Corps traces its beginning to November 10, 1775, when the Continental Congress passed a resolution stating that "two Battalions of Marines be raised" for service as landing forces with the naval fleet. The Revolutionary War ended in 1783, and the Marines were reactivated in 1798 by an act of Congress. The *Act for the Better Organization of the United States Marine Corps,* passed in 1834, stipulated that the Corps was a component of the Department of the Navy, as a sister service. The National Security Act of 1947 reaffirmed the Corps' status as an independent service.

Mission

The Marines have a unique mission statement among the branches of the armed forces, namely, that they "...shall, at any time, be liable to do duty in the forts and garrisons of the United States, on the seacoast, or any other duty on shore, as the President, at his discretion, shall direct." In this special capacity, the Marine Corps serves as an all-purpose, rapid-response task force.

Organization

The Marine Corps is a separate service within the Department of the Navy. Administered by a civilian Secretary of the Navy, the Corps is supervised by a military Commandant of the Marine Corps who is a member of the Joint Chiefs of Staff. The Marine Corps serves as an expeditionary force-in-readiness, responsible for rapid troop deployment for combined land, sea, and air operations. In addition to its primary responsibilities, the Marine Corps provides security on Navy ships and bases, and at U.S. embassies abroad.

The principal operating forces of the Marine Corps are the fleet Marine Forces and security forces. The Corps is combat-organized into Marine Air-Ground Task Forces (MAGTFs), which integrate a ground combat element, an aviation combat element, and a logistics combat element, under a common command element (CE), which is capable of operating independently or as part of a coalition. The smallest MAGTFs are Marine Expeditionary Units, which are components of the largest, the Marine Expeditionary Forces (MEFs). The three MEFs each combine a Division, an Air Wing, and a Logistics Group under an MEF Headquarters Group, and are stationed at Camp Lejeune, North Carolina; Camp Pendleton, California; and in Okinawa, Japan. There is also a Marine Forces Special Operations Group, consisting of 2,500 personnel, which is under the direction of the U.S. Special Operations Command.

Personnel

Current personnel strength of the Marine Corps is about 190,000 active duty and 40,000 Marine Corps Reserve members.

U.S. Navy

History
The Navy's origins began when, on October 13, 1775, the Continental Congress voted to fit out two sailing vessels for the purpose of intercepting transports carrying supplies to the British Army. The Constitution of the U.S., ratified in 1789, empowers Congress to "provide and maintain a Navy." From 1794 until 1798, administration of naval affairs was the responsibility of the Department of War. In 1798, Congress established the Department of the Navy. The National Security Act of 1947 created the Department of Defense, to include the military Departments.

Mission
The mission of the Navy is to maintain, train and equip combat-ready Naval forces capable of winning wars, deterring aggression and maintaining freedom of the seas.

Organization
The Department of the Navy is the maritime military force, responsible for deploying personnel on board ships, submarines and aircraft to strike on the sea or land. It is administered by a civilian secretary appointed by the President and supervised by a military Chief of Naval Operations appointed by the President with the consent of the Senate for a four year term. The Secretary and Chief together direct the Navy mission, and have responsibilities very similar to those of their counterparts in the Air Force and Army, recruiting and administering Navy personnel and providing trained forces to the Combatant Commands for use in military operations as directed by the Secretary of Defense. The Chief of Staff also serves as a member of the Joint Chiefs of Staff.

There are nine components of the operating forces: Fleet Forces Command (formerly Atlantic Fleet), Pacific Fleet, Naval Forces Central Command, Naval Forces Europe, Naval Network Warfare Command, Naval Special Warfare Command, Military Sealift Command, Operational Test and Evaluation Force, and the Navy Reserve. The Navy also has six active numbered fleets – Third, Fourth, Fifth, Sixth, Seventh, and Tenth Fleets, which are grouped under the Fleet Forces Command, the Pacific Fleet, Naval Forces Europe-Africa, and the Naval Forces Central Command. Currently, the Navy has about 280 deployable combat ships and over 3,700 aircraft. In 2007, a new *Cooperative Strategy for 21st Century Seapower* was adopted whereby the Navy, Coast Guard, and the Marine Corps work collectively with each other and international partners to prevent crises, or respond rapidly should one occur.

Personnel
Current personnel strength of the Navy is about 325,000 active duty members and 110,000 personnel in the Naval Ready Reserve.

National Oceanic and Atmospheric Administration Corps

History

The National Oceanic and Atmospheric Administration Commissioned Corps (NOAA Corps) traces its lineage to 1807 when President Thomas Jefferson signed a bill for the "Survey of the Coast." This resulted in formation of the U.S. Coast and Geodetic Survey (C&GS, or Coast Survey), the oldest scientific agency in the Federal government. The Coast Survey was made up of civilians, along with Army and Naval officers. With the outbreak of the Civil War, most military officers were withdrawn and the civilian surveyors, by virtue of their service on the war's front lines, were the predecessors of today's NOAA Corps. With the entry of the U.S. into the World War I, the commissioned service was formed on May 22, 1917 as the Coast and Geodetic Survey Corps, and, subsequently, as the Environmental Science Services Administration (ESSA) Corps from 1965 to 1970. The ESSA was transferred to newly established National Oceanic and Atmospheric Administration in October 1970 and the Corps was redesignated the NOAA Corps.

Mission

The mission of the NOAA Corps is to provide officers technically competent to assume positions of leadership and command in the National Oceanic and Atmospheric Administration and Department of Commerce programs and in the armed forces during times of war or national emergency.

Organization

The National Oceanic and Atmospheric Administration is an agency of the U.S. Department of Commerce. The NOAA Corps is directed by a Flag Officer who also serves as the Director of the Office of Marine and Aviation Operations which operates a wide variety of specialized aircraft and ships to conduct NOAA's environmental and scientific missions. Commissioned officers operate NOAA's fleet of research and survey vessels and aircraft; conduct field projects on land, at and under the sea, and in the air; manage NOAA observational and support facilities; serve as members or leaders of research efforts; and administer and manage various organizational elements throughout NOAA.

Personnel

The National Oceanic and Atmospheric Administration Corps has a currently authorized strength of 321 active duty commissioned officers.

NOTES

ABBREVIATIONS, ACRONYMS & GLOSSARY

ACA – [Patient Protection and] Affordable Care Act

AD – Active Duty

Aide-de-camp (ADC) – An officer who acts in the capacity of a confidential assistant to a flag officer or other high-ranking civilian official

Air Mobility Command (AMC) – The Air Force component of the U.S. Transportation Command

APHT – Applied Public Health Team

ASG – Assistant Surgeon General

ASH – Assistant Secretary for Health

As you were – The order to resume the previous activity

Attaché – An expert representative on the diplomatic staff of his/her country at a foreign capitol

Attention on deck – The call given by the officer who sees a senior officer entering the room

Aye, aye – The response to an order indicating that the order was heard, understood, and will be carried out

BOQ – Bachelor officer quarters

BPED – Base pay entry date

Bravo Zulu – The phonetic pronunciation of BZ, from the NATO signal codes, meaning "Well done"

BX – Base exchange

CAD – Call to active duty (date)

CAP – Capital Area Provider Team

Carry on – The order to resume the previous activity

CC – Commissioned Corps

CCMIS – Commissioned Corps Management Information System

CCPM – Commissioned Corps Personnel Manual

CCRF – Commissioned Corps Readiness Force

Chargé d' Affaires – The officer in charge of diplomatic business in the absence of the ambassador or minister

CO – Commanding officer

COER – Commissioned Officers' Effectiveness Report

Colors – The national flag; the distinguishing flag flown to indicate a ship's nationality; the Naval ceremonies of hoisting the national flag at 0800 and hauling it down at sunset

Commission – Written order granting an officer rank and authority; to activate a ship or station

Company grade – Refers to officers of the 0-1 to 0-3 grades in the Air Force, Army, and Marine Corps

CONUS – Continental United States

COSTEP – Commissioned Officer Student Training and Extern Program

COTA – Commissioned Officer Training Academy

CPO – Chief Professional Officer

CS – Civil Service

DCCPR – Division of Commissioned Corps Personnel and Readiness

DEERS – Defense Enrollment Eligibility Reporting System

DOD – Department of Defense

DSG – Deputy Surgeon General

DV – Distinguished visitor; also referred to as *the principal*

eCCIS – electronic Commissioned Corps Issuance System

Ensign – The national flag; the flag flown to indicate a military ship's nationality; the most junior commissioned officer rank in the Navy, Coast Guard, NOAA, and USPHS

EOD – Entry on duty

eOPF – electronic Official Personnel Folder

Field grade – Refers to officers of the 0-4 to 0-6 grades in the Air Force, Army, and Marine Corps

Flag officer – Admiral or General (pay grade 0-7 and above) in the uniformed services

General officer – General (pay grade 0-7 and above) in the Air Force, Army, and Marine Corps

Grade – The code corresponding with a service member's rank

Hail and farewell – A social function to welcome newcomers and bid farewell to those leaving a duty station

HHS – Department of Health and Human Services

HQ – Headquarters

HSO – Health Services Officer

Interoperability – The term used to indicate the capability of uniformed services to act in conjunction with one another to complete a mission

IOTC – Independent Officer Training Course

JFTR – Joint Federal Travel Regulations

JOAG – Junior Officer Advisory Group

Junior officer – Refers to officers of the 0-1 to 0-4 grades in the Coast Guard, Navy, NOAA, and PHS

Line officer – Refers to an officer who is trained to assume command in a combat situation

LUA – Local Uniform Authority

MAC – Military Airlift Command

Merchant ensign – The flag flown to indicate a merchant ship's nationality

Mess – The area or room where meals are served

MHT – Mental Health Team

MOLC – Minority Officers Liaison Council

Morning and evening colors – Naval term for the daily ceremony of raising and lowering the national flag

MPF – Military personnel flight

MRC – Medical Reserve Corps

MRE – Meal, ready-to-eat

MTF – Military Treatment Facility

NASA – National Aeronautics and Space Administration

NATO – North Atlantic Treaty Organization

NCO – Noncommissioned officer

NIST – National Incident Support Team

NOAA – National Oceanic and Atmospheric Administration

NRF – National Response Framework

OASH – Office of the Assistant Secretary for Health, HHS

OBC – Officer Basic Course

OCCFM – Office of Commissioned Corps Force Management

OCONUS – Outside the continental United States

ODU – Operational Dress Uniform

OFRD – Office of Force Readiness and Deployment

OIC – Officer in charge

OOD – Officer of the deck; a senior petty officer, warrant or commissioned officer who stands at the entry point to a ship, and who grants permission to come aboard or depart the ship

OPDIV – Agency/Operating Division/Program

OPF – Official personnel folder

OPM – Office of Personnel Management

ORA – Office of Reserve Affairs

OS – Office of the Secretary *or* Officer Statement

OSG – Office of the Surgeon General

PAC – Professional Advisory Committee

PAG – Professional Advisory Group

PAO – Public affairs officer

Pay grade – Alphanumeric designation that corresponds to the seniority of a service member; *O* designates a commissioned officer, *W* a warrant officer and *E* an enlisted member

PCS – Permanent change of (duty) station

PDS – Permanent Duty Station

PHS – Public Health Service

PO – Personnel Orders

PX – Post exchange (Army)

Quarterdeck – The area of a ship where the OOD stands watch; this is normally on the main deck near the gangway

Rank – The formal title of a grade or position

Rate – Naval term for an enlisted member's rank or pay grade

Rating – Naval term for an enlisted member's occupational specialty

RDF – Rapid Deployment Force

Ready Reserve Corps – The reserve component of the USPHS

Regular Corps – The career component of the PHS Commissioned Corps

Reveille and retreat – Army and Air Force term for the daily ceremony of raising and lowering the national flag

RIST – Regional Incident Support Team

ROG – Research Officers Group

RRP – Readiness and Response Program

SAT – Services Access Team

SDB – Service Dress Blue

Senior officer – Refers to officers at the 0-5 to 0-6 grades in the Coast Guard, Navy, NOAA, and PHS

SERNO – PHS Serial Number

SG – Surgeon General

SGPAC – Surgeon General's Policy Advisory Council

SW – Summer White

TDY – Temporary duty

The Principal – A flag officer or high-ranking official

TRANSCOM – U.S. Transportation Command

Very well – The reply of a senior officer to a junior officer's verbal report; never said by a junior to a senior officer

VOQ – Visiting officer quarters

XO – Executive officer, who is second in command

Zulu time – Greenwich Mean Time (GMT)

SELECTED REFERENCES

NOTE: Approximately one hundred sources of protocol, etiquette, and service standards information and regulations were used in the preparation of the *Public Health Service Officer's Guide, 2nd Edition.* The references which follow are cited references and/or among the more reliable information resources.

Books, Publications

Air Force Space Command. *'Til Wheels are Up.* Protocol Office. Luke Air Force Base. Unofficial protocol document of the US Air Force. 31 May 2002.

Baldrige L. *New Complete Guide to Executive Manners.* New York: Rawson Assoc., 1993.

Baldrige L. *New Manners for New Times.* New York: Scribner, 2003.

Benton JC. *Air Force Officer's Guide.* 35th Ed. Mechanicsburg, PA: Stackpole Books, 2008.

Cohen WA. *The Stuff of Heroes: The Eight Universal Laws of Leadership.* Longstreet Press, 2001.

Conetsco C, Hart A. *Service Etiquette.* 5th Ed. Annapolis: Naval Institute Press. 2009.

Connell RW, Mack WP. *Naval Ceremonies, Customs, and Traditions.* 6th Ed. Annapolis: Naval Institute Press, 2004.

Dalessandro RJ. *Army Officer's Guide.* 52nd Ed. Mechanicsburg, PA: Stackpole Books, 2013.

Department of the Air Force. *Handbook for Generals' Aides.* Air Force Manual 36-6. Headquarters. Washington, DC.

Department of the Army. *A Guide to Protocol and Etiquette for Official Entertainment.* Pamphlet 600-60. Headquarters. Washington, DC. 11 December 2001.

Department of the Army. *Army Leadership.* Field Manual No. 6-22. Headquarters. Washington, DC. 1 August 2012.

Department of the Army. *Drill and Ceremonies.* Field Manual No. TC 3-21.5. Headquarters. Washington, DC. 20 January 2012.

Department of the Army. *Preparing and Managing Correspondence.* Army Regulation 25-50. Headquarters. Washington, DC. 17 May 2013.

Department of the Army. *Salutes, Honors, and Visits of Courtesy.* Army Regulation 600-25. Headquarters. Washington, DC. 24 September 2004.

Department of the Navy. Naval School. Civil Engineer Corps Officers. *Mess Night Manual.* Port Hueneme, CA. August 1986.

Department of the Navy. *Navy Leadership Competency Model (NLCM).* Naval Education and Training Command.

Department of the Navy. *Social Usage and Protocol Handbook. A Guide for Personnel of the U.S. Navy.* OPNAVINST 1710.7A. Office of the Chief of Naval Operations. Washington, DC. 15 June 2001.

Drucker PF. *Essential Drucker: Management, the Individual and Society.* Routledge. 2001.

Gerras SJ, ed. *Strategic Leadership Primer.* 3rd Ed. Carlisle Barracks, PA: US Army War College, 2010.

Goleman D. *Emotional Intelligence: Why It Can Matter More Than IQ.* Bantam, 1995.

Goleman D. *Social Intelligence: The New Science of Human Relationships.* Bantam, 2006.

Hamowy R. *Government and Public Health in America.* Northampton, MA: E. Elgar Publishing, 2007.

Harvard Business Review. *Leadership Insights.* Boston, MA: Harvard Business School Publishing, 2010.

Harvard Business Review. *HBR's 10 Must Reads – On Leadership.* Boston, MA: Harvard Business Review Press, 2011.

Knoben JE, Knoben LH. *Executive Etiquette: Contemporary Etiquette and Business Practice for the Professional Person.* Hamilton, IL: Hamilton Press, 1990.

Kouzes JM, Posner BZ. *The Leadership Challenge.* 5th Ed. San Francisco: Wiley, 2012.

Maxwell JC. *The 5 Levels of Leadership.* New York: Center Street, 2011.

McComas LA. *The Naval Officer's Guide.* 12th Ed. Annapolis: Naval Institute Press, 2011.

Moore JH. *The Etiquette Advantage.* Nashville: Broadman & Holman Publishers, 1998.

Mullan F. *Plagues and Politics: The Story of the United States Public Health Service.* New York: Basic Books Publishers, 1989.

Office of Personnel Management. *Guide to Senior Executive Service Qualifications.* Washington, DC. September 2012.

Parascandola J. *A Brief History of the U.S. Public Health Service.* Anchor & Caduceus. Tampa: Faircount Publication, 2005.

Post P. *Emily Post's Etiquette.* 18th Ed. New York: Harper Collins Publishers, 2011.

Post P, Post P. *The Etiquette Advantage in Business.* 2nd Ed. New York: Harper Resource, 2005.

Robert HM, Honemann DH, Balch TJ. *Robert's Rules of Order.* 11th Ed. Philadelphia, PA: Da Capo Press, 2011.

Starling CC, Jackson WO. *West Point's Perspectives on Officership.* Cincinnati: Thomson Learning Custom Publishing, 2001.

US Air Force. *USAF Honor Guard: Basic Protocol, Honors, and Ceremonies.* Technical Training School. Washington, DC. December 2001.

US Air Force. *Protocol Primer.* AETC Pamphlet 90-101. Air Education and Training Command. Randolph, TX. 1 November 1995.

US Army War College. *Basics from the Barracks: Military Etiquette and Protocol.* Carlisle Barracks, PA: US Army War College. 2011.

US Military Academy. *Guide to Military Dining-in.* Protocol Office. West Point, NY.

Articles

Ambler G. *10 Characteristics of an Effective Vision.* www.georgeambler.com. Feb. 3, 2013.

Beck R, Harter J. *Why Managers Are So Rare.* HBR Blog Network, March 13, 2014.

Clinton JJ. *Public Health Service: Celebrating Our 200th Birthday.* The Officer. January-February, 1998.

Collins J. *Level 5 Leadership: The Triumph of Humility and Fierce Resolve.* Harvard Business Review, July 2005.

Cuddy AJC, Kohut M, Neffinger J. *Connect, Then Lead.* Harvard Business Review. July-August 2013.

Groves KS. *Integrating Leadership Development and Succession Planning Best Practices.* Journal of Management Development. 2007; 26: 239-60.

Koop CE, Ginzburg HM. *The Revitalization of the Public Health Service Commissioned Corps.* Public Health Reports. March-April, 1989.

APPENDICES

APPENDIX A.   Planning for
             Awards/Change of Command/
               Promotion/Retirement Ceremony
             Administrative Information
             Ceremony Components
             Ceremony Personnel
             Facility Arrangements
             Reception Arrangements

APPENDIX B.   Planning a Dining-Out
             Administrative Information
             Dining-Out Components
             Dining-Out Personnel
             Facility Arrangements
             Meal and Reception Arrangements

APPENDIX C.   Planning a Formal Reception
             Administrative Information
             Reception Components
             Reception Personnel
             Facility Arrangements
             Reception Arrangements

APPENDIX D.   Planning for a Distinguished Visitor
             Administrative Information
             Transportation
             Accommodations
             Pre-Arrival Preparations
             Event Arrangements & Personnel
             Reception Arrangements

Planning for
Awards/Change of Command/Promotion/Retirement

EVENT NAME: _____

DATE, TIME: _____

PLACE: _____ RESERVATION:_____

SPONSOR: _____

PROGRAM COORDINATOR: _____

PRESIDING OFFICER: _____

HONORED GUEST: _____

HONORED GUEST SPOUSE: _____

MASTER/MISTRESS OF CEREMONY: _____

SPEAKERS [ATTACH LIST WITH CONFIRMATION, CONTACT INFORMATION]

A. CEREMONY COMPONENTS

_√_ **TYPE OF CEREMONY**

_____ AWARDS CEREMONY

     _____ AWARDEES AND RECOGNITION [ATTACH LIST]

     _____ AWARDS APPROVED, RECEIVED AND READY

_____ CHANGE OF COMMAND

     _____ SG, ACTING SG, HHS OFFICIAL: _____

     _____ CHIEF PROFESSIONAL OFFICER: _____

     _____ OTHER, SPECIFY: _____

_____ PROMOTION CEREMONY

     _____ PROMOTION ORDERS READY

     _____ RANK INSIGNIA

_____ RETIREMENT CEREMONY

     _____ AWARD RECOGNITION

     _____ RETIREE BIOGRAPHY

     _____ RETIREMENT ORDERS

     _____ RETIREMENT GIFTS/PRESENTATIONS

√ ITEM COMPLETE & NOTES

_____ BRIEFING FOLDER

_____ INVITATIONS

_____ PROGRAM

_____ PROGRAM PRINTED

_____ PUBLICITY

_____ SCRIPT

B. CEREMONY PERSONNEL

√ ITEM COMPLETE & NOTES

_____ PLANNING COMMITTEE

_____ MEMBERS AND DUTIES ASSIGNED [ATTACH LIST]

_____ AIDES, ASSISTANTS

_____ HONOR CADRE

_____ MUSIC ENSEMBLE

_____ PHOTOGRAPHER

_____ USHERS

C. FACILITY ARRANGEMENTS

√ ITEM COMPLETE & NOTES

_____ FACILITY CONTACT

_____ FLAGS / STANDS

_____ MICROPHONES

_____ MUSIC [TAPED]

_____ PARKING

_____ PODIUM

_____ ROOM DIAGRAM

_____ STAGE SEATING

_____ STAGE TABLE

D. RECEPTION ARRANGEMENTS

__√__ ITEM COMPLETE & NOTES

_____ BEVERAGES [ATTACH LIST]

_____ CAKE, FOOD, SPECIAL ORDER [ATTACH LIST]

_____ CENTERPIECES, SPECIFY: _____

_____ MENU [ATTACH]

_____ PLACE CARDS [HEAD TABLE]

_____ RECEIVING LINE

_____ TABLES/SEATING [ATTACH SCHEMATIC]

Planning a Dining-Out

EVENT NAME: _____

DATE, TIME: _____

PLACE: _____ RESERVATION: _____

SPONSOR: _____

PROGRAM COORDINATOR: _____

PRESIDING OFFICER: _____

MISTER / MADAM VICE: _____

HONORED GUEST / SPEAKER: _____

HONORED GUEST SPOUSE: _____

A. DINING-OUT COMPONENTS

√   ITEM COMPLETE & NOTES

_____ CHIMES

_____ GAVEL

_____ GIFTS

_____ GROG BOWL

_____ INVITATIONS

_____ INVOCATION

_____ MENU

_____ MENU PRINTED

_____ PROGRAM

_____ PROGRAM PRINTED

_____ PUBLICITY

_____ SCRIPT

_____ TOASTS, PREARRANGED

B. DINING-OUT PERSONNEL

___√___ ITEM COMPLETE & NOTES

_____ PLANNING COMMITTEE

    _____ MEMBERS AND DUTIES ASSIGNED [ATTACH LIST]

    _____ BAGPIPER

    _____ HONOR CADRE

    _____ MUSIC ENSEMBLE

    _____ PHOTOGRAPHER

    _____ TREASURER

C. FACILITY ARRANGEMENTS

___√___ ITEM COMPLETE & NOTES

    _____ FACILITY CONTACT

    _____ PRE–DINNER RECEPTION ROOM

    _____ DINING ROOM

    _____ FLAGS / STANDS

    _____ MICROPHONES

    _____ PARKING

    _____ ROOM DIAGRAM [ATTACH SCHEMATIC]

    _____ TABLES / SEATING [ATTACH SCHEMATIC]

        _____ GENERAL

        _____ HEAD, VICE TABLE

        _____ POW / MIA TABLE

D. MEAL AND RECEPTION ARRANGEMENTS

___√___ ITEM COMPLETE & NOTES

    _____ BEVERAGES [ALCOHOL / NONALCOHOL]

    _____ CAKE, FOOD, SPECIAL ORDER [ATTACH LIST]

    _____ CENTERPIECES

    _____ PLACE CARDS [HEAD TABLE]

    _____ PLACE SETTINGS [FORMAL]

    _____ TABLES / SEATING

Planning a Formal Reception

EVENT NAME: _____

DATE, TIME: _____

PLACE: _____ RESERVATION:_____

SPONSOR: _____

PROGRAM COORDINATOR: _____

HOST OFFICER: _____

HONORED GUEST: _____

HONORED GUEST SPOUSE: _____

A. RECEPTION COMPONENTS

   __√__ **ITEM COMPLETE & NOTES**

      _____ INVITATIONS

      _____ HORS D'OEUVRES MENU

      _____ PUBLICITY

      _____ RECEIVING LINE

         _____ LOCATION IN ROOM

         _____ ORDER OF PRECEDENCE

         _____ FLAGS/STANDS/TABLE

         _____ AIDE/ANNOUNCER

         _____ OFFICER, END OF LINE

B. RECEPTION PERSONNEL

   __√__ **ITEM COMPLETE & NOTES**

      _____ PLANNING COMMITTEE

         _____ MEMBERS AND DUTIES ASSIGNED [ATTACH LIST]

         _____ HONOR CADRE

         _____ MUSIC ENSEMBLE

         _____ PHOTOGRAPHER

C. FACILITY ARRANGEMENTS

__√__ ITEM COMPLETE & NOTES

_____ FACILITY CONTACT

_____ FLAGS / STANDS

_____ MICROPHONES

_____ PARKING

_____ ROOM DIAGRAM

D. RECEPTION ARRANGEMENTS

__√__ ITEM COMPLETE & NOTES

_____ BEVERAGES [ALCOHOL / NONALCOHOL]

_____ CAKE, FOOD, SPECIAL ORDER [ATTACH LIST]

_____ CENTERPIECES

_____ DECORATIONS

_____ ROOM ARRANGEMENT

_____ TABLES / SEATING

Planning for a Distinguished Visitor

DV RANK, FULL NAME: _____

DUTY TITLE: _____

DUTY STATION: _____

MAILING ADDRESS: _____

DV CONTACT NUMBERS: _____

DATES OF VISIT: _____

PURPOSE OF VISIT: _____

OFFICIAL PARTY MEMBERS [INCLUDE SPOUSE IF TRAVELING WITH DV]

RANK	FULL NAME	DUTY TITLE, DUTY STATION

AIDE: _____

ESCORT OFFICER: _____

PROGRAM COORDINATOR: _____

A. TRANSPORTATION

   _√_ **ITEM COMPLETE & NOTES**

   _____ AIRLINE RESERVATION CONFIRMATION NUMBER: _____

   _____ VEHICLE RESERVATION CONFIRMATION NUMBER: _____

FLIGHT DATA

	AIRPORT	DATE	TIME	AIRLINE	FLIGHT #
ARRIVAL					
DEPARTURE					

VEHICLE DATA

GSA/RENTAL CO. NAME:
GSA/RENTAL CO. ADDRESS:
GSA/RENTAL CO. TELEPHONE NUMBER:
CAR MFR./LICENSE NUMBER:

B. ACCOMMODATIONS

LODGING DATA

BASE QUARTERS / HOTEL NAME:
BASE / HOTEL ADDRESS:
BASE / HOTEL TELEPHONE NUMBER:
CHECK–IN DATE / TIME:
CHECK–OUT DATE / TIME:
RESERVATION CONFIRMATION NUMBER:

C. PRE-ARRIVAL PREPARATIONS

__√__ ITEM COMPLETE & NOTES

_____ GROUND TRANSPORTATION : _____

_____ DRIVER ASSIGNED: _____

_____ DRIVER BRIEFED AND KNOWS DIRECTIONS

_____ SENIOR OFFICER AT ARRIVAL: _____

_____ FOLIO FOR DV [ITINERARY, CONTACT INFO., NAMES, NOTES]

D. EVENT ARRANGEMENTS & PERSONNEL

__√__ ITEM COMPLETE & NOTES

_____ FACILITY CONTACT

_____ FLAGS / STANDS

_____ MICROPHONES, MUSIC [TAPED]

_____ PARKING

_____ PODIUM, TABLE [HEAD], SEATING ASSIGNMENTS

_____ ROOM DIAGRAM [ATTACH SCHEMATIC]

_____ PLANNING COMMITTEE

_____ MEMBERS AND DUTIES ASSIGNED [ATTACH LIST]

_____ DV GREETER _____

_____ HONOR CADRE

_____ MUSIC ENSEMBLE

_____ PHOTOGRAPHER

E. RECEPTION ARRANGEMENTS

See *Planning a Formal Reception,* Appendix C.

INDEX

Abbreviations, 179

Acronyms, 179

Address, forms of

civilian, 129

conversation, 121

correspondence, 123

introductions, 128

uniformed service, 5-12, 41-43

Affordable Care Act, 162

Aide-de-camp, 89-96

Aiguillette, 24, 91, 93

Air Force, US

overview, 170

ranks, 5-12

Appearance and grooming, 13, 14

Appendices, 185-194

awards ceremony, 186

change of command, 186

dining-out, 189

distinguished visitor, 193

formal reception, 191

promotion ceremony, 186

retirement ceremony, 186

Appointment board, 97

Arch of swords, 87

Army, US

leadership requirements, 40

overview, 172

ranks, 5-12

Assistant Secretary for Health, 153

Attention, coming to, 44

Awards, decorations, 19-23

order of precedence,19-22

presentation ceremony, 54, 186

Badges, 23

Bags, carrying, 14

Bell ringing, honors, 50, 58, 65

Boards, Commissioned Corps, 97

Business cards, 117-119

Calls, military, 120

Cards

attaché, 120

business, 117

calling, 120

menu, 145

personal, 120

place, 145

Cell phone etiquette, 133

Ceremonial uniforms, 15

Ceremony

awards, 54, 186

change of command, 57, 186

dining-in, dining-out, 73, 189

dinners, official, 80

funeral honors, 70

official, protocol, 54

Old Glory Flag, 67

promotion, 60, 186

receptions, 80, 191

retirement, 63, 186

social, protocol, 73

wedding, 87

Change of command, 57, 186

Chief professional officer, 98

Civilian forms of address, 129

Coast Guard, US

    overview, 173

    ranks, 5-12

Coin, PHS, 167

Color guard, *See* Honor Cadre

Commissioned officer, *See* Officer

Communications

    business cards, 117

    calls and cards, 120

    conversation, 121

    correspondence, 123

    devices, carrying, 14

    forms of address, 129

    greetings and introductions, 127

    invitations, 81

    presentation, speaking, 122, 130

    telecommunications, 132

Conventions, 138

Conversation, 121-123

    addressing officers, 121

    effective speaking, 122, 130

    greetings and introductions, 127

Core values, 25

Correspondence, 123-126

    composition, 124

    elements, 125

    formats, 126

Courtesy and protocol, 41-53

    address and greeting, 41

    attention, coming to, 44

    flag etiquette, 45

    funeral honors, 70

    handshake, 43

    headgear, 48

    position of honor, 49

    precedence of military, 49, 83

    rendering honors, 50

    saluting, 47, 50

    ship boarding, 53

    titles of rank, 43

Cultural competence, 3

Culture, traditions, protocol, 3

Customs and protocol, 4

Department of Defense, 168

Department of HHS, 153

Deployment, 112-115

    basic standards, 113

    preparation, 115

    response teams, 114, 115

Deputy Surgeon General, 155, 158

Dining manners, 142-151

Dining-out, dining-in, 73-79, 189

Dinner dress uniforms, 15

Dinners

    dining-out, 73-79, 189

    guest of honor, 78, 84, 85

    host, 84, 85, 150

    invitations, 81

    official, 80

    order of precedence, 83, 84

    receiving line, 83

    receptions, 83, 191

    restaurant, 149

    seating arrangements, 84, 145

    table manners, 142-151

    table settings, 141-145

    toasts, 86

Distinguished visitor, 94, 110, 193

Division of Civilian Volunteer
Medical Reserve Corps, 154

Division of Commissioned Corps
Personnel and Readiness, 154

Division of Science and
Communications, 154

Division of Systems Integration, 154

Electronic mail etiquette, 132

Emergency response teams, 114, 115

Emotional intelligence, 30

Enlisted personnel
grades, insignia, ratings, 6-8
qualifications, 6
titles, 41, 42

Escort officer, 90, 93-96

Essentials, uniformed service, 1-24

Flag etiquette, US, PHS, 45-48
displaying, 46
folding, US, 48
funeral presentation, 72
in mourning, 47
Old Glory ceremony, 67
over casket, 70
parading, 47
presentation of, 101
Public Health Service, 166

Foreign stations, social calls, 120

Funeral honors, 70-72

General purpose uniforms, 15

Global public health, 153, 156, 165

Glossary, 179

Grades, uniformed services, 5-12

Greetings
and address, 41, 127

and introductions, 127, 128

Grooming and appearance, 13, 14

Guest of honor
dining-out, 78
receiving line, 83, 84
seating arrangement, 84, 85

Handshake, 43

Headgear
protocol, 48
types, 17

Heritage, 4

History
Ofc., Surgeon General, 155-158
Public Health Service, 163-166

Honor Cadre, 100-102

Honor position, 49

Honors, rendering, 50, 58, 65

Host/Hostess
receiving line, 83, 84
restaurant, duties of, 149-151
seating arrangement, 85

Insignia
commissioned officer, 5-12, 18
enlisted, 6-8
warrant officer, 5, 9

Introductions, 128

Invitations, 81, 82

Junior Officer Advisory Group, 103

Leadership, 25-40
Army requirements model, 40
competencies, 34
core values, 25
cultural competence, 3
emotional intelligence, 30
management, 29

Navy competency model, 35
officership, 26
OPM qualifications, 34
PHS competency model, 40
principles, 25, 36-40
theory, 28-33
Letter, correspondence, 123-126
Liaison, Commissioned Corps, 104
Management and leadership, 29, 30
Manners, dining, 142-151
Marine Corps, US
overview, 175
ranks, 5-12
Medals, wearing of, 22, 23
Medical Reserve Corps, 154
Medical review board, 97
Meetings, 134-140
chairperson, 135
conventions,138
office appointments, 137
parliamentary procedure,138
participants, 136
Memoranda, 123-126
Military courtesy and protocol,
See Courtesy and protocol
Military funeral honors, 70-72
Military services, precedence, 49, 83
Military wedding ceremony, 87, 88
Minority Officers Liaison, 105
Mission, USPHS, 3, 152
Morning and evening colors, 52
Music Ensemble, 106
Name tag, 17
National Anthem, 47
National Prevention Council, 155

National Response Framework, 112
Navy, US
leadership competency, 35
overview, 176
ranks, 5-12
NOAA Corps, US
overview, 177
ranks, 5-12
Noncommissioned officer, 6
Office appointments, 137
Office of Surgeon General, 154-158
Deputy SG, 155, 158
first Surgeon General, 156
history, 155
organization, 154
responsibilities, 155
tenures, 157
Officer
agency assignments, 158
aide-de-camp, 89
chief professional, 98
company grade, 5
core values, 25
device standards, 18
escort, 90, 93
field grade, 5
grades, 5-12
grooming, 13, 14
headgear, 17, 48
Honor Cadre, 100
insignia, 5-12, 18
leadership, 25-40
line and non-line, 5
noncommissioned, 6
officership, 2, 26

personal appearance, 13, 14
professional, 2
protocol, 90, 110
qualifications, 5
ranks, 5, 10-12
titles, 41-43
uniform standards, 15-24
warrant, 5, 9, 42
Officership, 2, 26
Official calls, 120
Official ceremony protocol, 54-72
Old Glory flag ceremony, 67
OPM core qualifications, 34
Order of precedence, *See*
  Precedence
Organization
  military services, 168
  US Public Health Service, 152
Parliamentary procedure, 138-140
Patient Protection and Affordable
  Care Act, 162
PHS, CC seals, 166
PHS coin, 167
PHS leadership model, 40
PHS March and Fanfare, 167
Place settings, 141-145
Pledge of Allegiance, 47
Policy Advisory Council, SG, 116
Position of honor, 49
Precedence
  awards and decorations, 19
  ceremonial, social, 83
  guest of honor, 83-85
  host, 83-85
  receiving line, 83, 84

seating arrangements, 84, 145
  uniformed service, 49, 83
Presentation of awards, 54, 186
Presentations, speaking, 122, 130
Professional advisory committee, 108
Professional advisory group, 109
Professional officer, 2
Promotion boards, 97
Promotion ceremony, 60, 186
Protocol
  and courtesy, 41
  and tradition, 4
  officer, 90, 110
  official ceremony, 54
  social ceremony, 73
Public Health Service, US, 152-167
  agency assignments, 158-162
  Asst. Secretary for Health, 153
  coin, 167
  core values, 25
  customs, protocol, 4
  flag, 166
  Health and Human Services, 153
  history, 163-165
  introduction, 1-5
  March and Fanfare, 167
  mission, 3, 152
  Office of Surgeon General, 154
  officership, 26
  organization, 153, 154
  professional officer, 2
  Ready Reserve Corps, 162
  Regular Corps, 162
  seal, 166
  traditions, heritage, 4

Ranks, 5-12
    commissioned officer, 5, 10-12
    enlisted personnel, 6-8
    noncommissioned officer, 6
    titles of, 41-43
    warrant officer, 5, 9
Readiness force, 112-115
    basic standards, 113
    preparation, 115
    response teams, 114, 115
Ready Reserve Corps, 162
Receiving line, 83, 84
Receptions, 80, 83, 84
    dinners, official, 80, 191
    invitations, 81
    order of precedence, 83
    receiving line, 83
References, 183
Regular Corps, 162
Rendering honors, 50, 58, 65
Restaurant dining, 149-151
Retirement ceremony, 63, 186
Reveille and retreat, 52
Ribbons, wearing of, 22, 23
Saluting, 50-53
    funeral honors, 70, 72
    Honor Cadre, 101
    National anthem, 47
    Pledge of allegiance, 47
    protocol, 50-53
    rendering honors, 50
    ship boarding, 53
Seal, official
    Public Health Service, 166
    PHS Commissioned Corps, 166

Seating arrangements, 84, 145
Ship boarding, 53
Sideboys
    rendering honors, 50, 58, 65
Social calls, 120
Social ceremony protocol, 73-88
Speaking, effective, 122, 130
Special duty, 89-116
    aide-de-camp, 89
    boards, 97
    chief professional officer, 98
    escort officer, 90, 93
    Honor Cadre, 100
    Jr. Officer Advisory Group, 103
    liaison, CC, 104
    Minority Officers Liaison, 105
    Music Ensemble, 106
    Policy advisory council, 116
    Professional advisory
        committee, 108
    protocol officer, 90, 110
    readiness force, 112
Special purpose uniforms, 15
Stars, ribbon, medal, 23
Stationery, 124
Surgeon General, 154-158
    introduction, 1
    Medallion, 23
    Nat'l. Prevention Council, 155
    Office of, 154-158
    Policy Advisory Council, 116
    Woodworth JM, 156
Sword
    presenting colors, 101
    wedding, arch of, 87

Table manners, 142-151
Table protocol, 141-151
  restaurant dining, 149-151
  table manners, 142-151
  table settings, 141-145
Table settings, 141-145
Telecommunications, 132, 133
  Cell phone, 133
  Electronic mail, 132
  Telephone, 133
Telephone etiquette, 133
Theory of leadership, 28-33
Titles
  civilian, 129
  military, 41-43
Toasts
  dining-out, 77
  dinners, official, 86
  table protocol, 149
Tradition, culture, protocol, 3, 4
Travel, uniform, 16
Uniformed service
  address and greeting, 41
  attention, coming to, 44
  courtesy and protocol, 41-53
  essentials, 1
  flag etiquette, 45
  funeral honors, 70
  handshake, 43
  headgear, 17, 48

organizations, 168-177
position of honor, 49
precedence, military, 49, 83
rendering honors, 50, 58, 65
saluting, 50
ship boarding, 53
titles of rank, 43
use of first names, 41
Uniforms, 15-24
  aiguillettes, 24, 91, 93
  awards, decorations, 19-23
  badges, 23
  classifications, 15
  considerations, 17
  headgear, 17
  insignia, 18
  name tag, 17
  policy, 16
  Reserve, retired officers, 16
  ribbons, medals, 22
  standards, 15
  stars, 23
  travel, 16
Warrant officer
  grades, 5, 9
  qualifications, 5
  titles, 42
Wedding ceremony, 87, 88
Woodworth JM, 156
Working uniforms, 15